ACTIVE MATHEMATICS 1

ACTIVE MATHEMATICS

Pupils' book 1   0 582 08439 3
Teacher's guide 1   0 582 08444 X

B. V. Hony

Pupils' book 2   0 582 08440 7
Teacher's guide 2   0 582 08445 8

B. V. Hony

Pupils' book 3   0 582 08441 5
Teacher's guide 3   0 582 08446 6

B. V. Hony and D. A. Turner

Pupils' book 4   0 582 08442 3
Teacher's guide 4   0 582 08447 4

D. A. Turner, B. V. Hony, I. A. Potts, K. D. Oakley and P. S. Lane

Pupils' book 5   0 582 08443 1
Teacher's guide 5   0 582 08448 2

D. A. Turner, B. V. Hony, I. A. Potts and K. D. Oakley

ACTIVE MATHEMATICS 1

B. V. Hony

Oundle School

LONGMAN

Longman Group UK Limited
*Longman House, Burnt Mill, Harlow, Essex CM20 2JE, England
and Associated Companies throughout the world.*

First published by Active Publications 1988
© Active Publications

Second edition first published by Longman Group UK Limited 1992
© Longman Group UK Limited

First published 1992
Fourth impression 1995
ISBN 0 582 08439 3

Set in Times by Ellis Associates
Produced by Longman Singapore Publications Pte Ltd
Printed in Singapore

The publisher's policy is to use paper manufactured from
sustainable forests.

TO THE USER OF THIS BOOK

You should enjoy using this book, especially if you like fast things, large things, interesting things or challenging things. You will be taught the tools of the maths trade and how to use them.

The tools of the trade

- To calculate on paper, in your head and with a calculator.
- To explain on paper what you are doing and how you are doing it.
- To use the basic skills of maths.

Using the tools of the trade

- To compare the sizes of numbers and quantities.
- To make scale drawings.
- To read scales and to use simple graphs.
- To work out speeds, area, length, volume, costs and profits.
- To use algebra to solve problems.
- To solve simple science problems.
- To investigate problems which may not have a single answer.
- To do project work.

About this book

Each chapter contains brief notes on the principles involved, followed by worked EXAMPLES of every type of problem. The REMEMBER boxes give useful hints. ACTIVITIES help to apply the principles.

The problems in the EXERCISES are graded and include some real challenges in the MASTERMINDER sections.

Learn more about the way maths can be applied in the COURSEWORK pages (marked by a grey bar down the edge of the page).

Finally, have some fun with the PUZZLERS at the end of each chapter.

ACKNOWLEDGEMENTS

The author would like to thank his wife for her tireless support and encouragement from the inception of this work, his father for providing so many ideas for the Puzzlers, Geoff Beckett for writing the appendix on Sets, Douglas Butler, John Hewitson, Keith Oakley, Robert Trigger and Chris Humphries, to name but a few who have offered invaluable advice during the development of the material, and last, but by no means least, the team from Longman, Nina Konrad, Sophie Clark and Hendrina Ellis, who launched this edition.

Photographs

Allsport 23 (top centre right), 138; The Associated Press 57; Barnabys Picture Library 101; Blackpool Tourism 160 left; Bruce Coleman 23 (top left), 23 (top centre left); Collections 54, 167; Colorsport 23 (top right); Dunwich Museum 137; Mary Evans Picture Library 14 (bottom), 156; The Ronald Grant Archive 49; Insight Picture Library 24 (right); Lockheed 100; London Transport Museum 68; Mid Sussex Times 34; NASA 136; Peterborough Evening Telegraph 23 (bottom left); Science Photo Library 14 (top), 139; Frank Spooner Pictures 140 (right and left); World Flying Disc Federation – photo: Jeff Garlick 23 (right); ZEFA Picture Library 13, 24 (left), 160 (centre and right).
Cover Launch of Shuttle Discovery on 13th March 1989, at the beginning of mission STS-29. Science Photo Library.

Active Mathematics and the National Curriculum

Level	4	5	6	7	8	9	10
Book 1	■	■	■				
Book 2		■	■	■			
Book 3			■	■	■		
Book 4				■	■	■	
Book 5							■

CONTENTS

CONTENTS

1 ARITHMETIC I

1.1 The four rules of number

In this first section we are going to look at the basic 'tools of the trade' – adding, subtracting, multiplying and dividing.

■ EXAMPLE 1

Which, of **a**, **b** and **c**, has a different answer from the other two?
a $412 + 94 + 5$ **b** $424 + 26 + 62$ **c** $395 + 9 + 107$

Arrange the digits in the correct column:

a	412	**b**	424	**c**	395
	94		26		9
+	5	+	62	+	107
	511		512		511

So **b** has the answer which is different.

■ EXAMPLE 2

Find $2173 - 986$.

Arrange digits in the correct column:

$$
\begin{array}{r}
2173 \\
-\ 986 \\
\hline
1187
\end{array}
$$

$2173 - 986 = 1187$

■ EXAMPLE 3

Work out $513 - 224 - 36$.

First subtract 224 from 513:

$$
\begin{array}{r}
513 \\
-\ 224 \\
\hline
289
\end{array}
$$

Next subtract 36 from 289:

$$
\begin{array}{r}
289 \\
-\ 36 \\
\hline
253
\end{array}
$$

$513 - 224 - 36 = 253$

■ EXAMPLE 4

Find 236×42.

Set it out like this:

$$
\begin{array}{r}
236 \\
\times\ 42 \\
\hline
9440 \\
472 \\
\hline
9912
\end{array}
$$

$(236 \times 40 = 9440)$
$(236 \times 2 = 472)$
$236 \times 42 = 9912$

■ EXAMPLE 5

What is $4352 \div 17$?

$$
\begin{array}{r}
256 \\
17\overline{)4352} \\
34 \\
\hline
95 \\
85 \\
\hline
102 \\
102 \\
\hline
000
\end{array}
$$

$(2 \times 17 = 34)$
$(5 \times 17 = 85)$
$(6 \times 17 = 102)$
$4352 \div 17 = 256$

NOTE

First, work out anything inside **brackets.**
Second, **multiply** and **divide**.
Third, **add** and **subtract**.

■ EXAMPLE 6

Find $500 - 24 \times 7$.

Work out the multiplication first:
$500 - 24 \times 7$
$=\ 500 - 168$
$=\ 332$

■ EXAMPLE 7

What is $600 \div (90 - 66)$?

Work out what is inside the brackets first, then divide:
$600 \div (90 - 66)$
$=\ 600 \div 24$
$=\ 25$

—— Exercise 1

For each of these questions, find which, of **a**, **b** and **c**, has a different answer from the other two.

1 a $357 + 95 + 217$ **b** $524 + 127 + 8$ **c** $787 + 35 - 153$

2 a $286 + 148 + 109$ **b** $724 + 87 - 269$ **c** $804 - 176 - 86$

3 a $2475 - 1913$ **b** $7091 - 6519$ **c** $4470 - 3898$

4 a $1282 - 957$ **b** $403 - 79$ **c** $1004 - 679$

5 a $736 + 94 - 355$ **b** $376 + 187 - 98$ **c** $432 + 71 - 38$

6 a $945 - 387 - 192$ **b** $817 - 356 - 85$ **c** $724 - 67 - 291$

7 a 763×4 **b** 436×7 **c** 338×9

8 a 273×8 **b** 177×12 **c** 168×13

9 a 408×16 **b** 286×23 **c** 192×34

10 a 527×32 **b** 136×124 **c** 132×127

11 a $2576 \div 8$ **b** $1660 \div 5$ **c** $2988 \div 9$

12 a $9261 \div 7$ **b** $15876 \div 12$ **c** $18536 \div 14$

13 a $4248 \div 18$ **b** $3198 \div 13$ **c** $3936 \div 16$

14 a $4745 \div 13$ **b** $5475 \div 15$ **c** $6750 \div 18$

15 a $110 - 12 \times 9$ **b** $60 - 464 \div 8$ **c** $(200 - 176) \div 8$

16 a $146 + 38 \times 8$ **b** $192 + 1456 \div 7$ **c** $6 \times (34 + 41)$

MASTERMINDERS

17 a $33 \times 6 - 48$ **b** $616 \div 8 + 63$ **c** $9600 \div (45 + 19)$

18 a $24 \times (86 + 39)$ **b** $(111 - 86) \times (205 - 61)$ **c** $(54 + 26) \times (127 - 82)$

19 a $224 \div (80 - 52)$ **b** $(197 + 91) \div (50 - 14)$ **c** $(509 + 366) \div (77 + 48)$

20 a $34 \times 8 + 420 \div 15$ **b** $18 \times 17 - 210 \div 35$ **c** $5400 \div 24 + 2000 \div 16$

—— Problem solving

You should solve problems in three stages. First, write down in **words** what you are trying to find. Second, show all your **working**. And third, write down the **answer**.

> *REMEMBER*
>
> [W]   Words
> [W]   Working
> [A]   Answer

■ *EXAMPLE 8*

The diameters of the Sun and two planets are shown here:

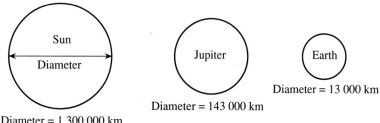

a How many times is (i) Jupiter wider than the Earth and (ii) the Sun wider than the Earth?

b If the largest star, called a Red Supergiant, is 2700 times wider than the Sun, find its diameter.

a (i) [W]   Number of times Jupiter is wider than the Earth

   [W] $= 143\,000 \div 13\,000$

   [A] $= 11$ times

  (ii) [W]   Number of times the Sun is wider than the Earth

   [W] $= 1\,300\,000 \div 13\,000$

   [A] $= 100$ times

b   [W]   Diameter of Red Supergiant

   [W] $= 2700 \times 1\,300\,000$ km

   [A] $= 3\,510\,000\,000$ km

        (This is 3510 million kilometres.)

⎯ Exercise 2

1 The cheapest new car costs £5000. If a Rolls Royce costs 19 times as much, how much does it cost?

2 If the population of Britain is 56 500 000 and China has 17 times as many people, what is the population of China?

3 Two railway lines are shown here:
   a How many times further is the longer journey?
   b How many times longer does the longer journey take?

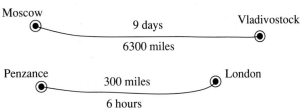

4 The Caspian Sea (the largest 'lake' on Earth) has an area of 375 000 km^2.
  Lake Windermere (the largest lake in the UK) has an area of 15 km^2.
  How many times larger is the Caspian Sea than Lake Windermere?

5 The highest waterfall on Earth is in Venezuela and is 950 m high. How many times higher is this than the Telecom Tower, which is 190 m high?

6 The heaviest whale has a mass of 192 tonnes, which is 32 times greater than the heaviest elephant. How heavy is the elephant?

7 In 1990 the world population was estimated to have been 5390 million. If this is 7 times more than in 1690, what was the population in 1690?

8 A woman has a mass of 56 kg and her brain has a mass of 1400 g. How many times greater is her body mass than her brain mass?

9 A cod has a mass of 10 kg. Its brain has a mass of 2 g. How many times heavier is its body mass than its brain mass?

10 This is a Stegosaurus, which is reputed to have been the 'most brainless animal ever'. Its mass was 1750 kg. If this was 25 000 times greater than its brain mass, how big was its brain?

Enter your results from Questions 8, 9 and 10 on a suitable table.

11 A van has a mass of 1935 kg when empty. It is loaded with 240 kg of cement, 150 kg of sand and 600 kg of bricks. If the mass of the driver is 75 kg, find the total mass.

12 The population of York is 105 000. Find the population of each of the following:
a Bradford, if it has 185 000 more people than York.
b Leeds, if it has 397 000 more people than York.
c Scarborough, if it has 61 000 fewer people than York.
d Harrogate, if it has 39 000 fewer people than York.

13 The height of Mount Everest is 8840 m above sea level. Find the height of each of the following:
a Mont Blanc, if it is 4030 m lower than Mount Everest.
b Snowdon, if it is 3725 m lower than Mont Blanc.
c Herefordshire Beacon, if it is 745 m lower than Snowdon.
d Shakespeare's Cliff, if it is 236 m lower than Herefordshire Beacon.

14 At 2 pm there are 2754 people inside a football ground. Between this time and the kick-off at 3 pm, 11 times this number of people arrive. If no more people arrive after that, find:
a The total number of spectators at the match.
b The number of tickets that were not used if this was an all-ticket match for which 36 000 tickets were printed.
c The attendance figure at a reserve-team match on the following Saturday, if the attendance figure was 18 times less than at the above match.

15 A girl's pencil case has a mass of 230 g when full and 35 g when empty. It contains 4 pens of mass 15 g each and 15 pencils. Find:
a The total mass of the contents.
b The total mass of the pens.
c The total mass of the pencils.
d The mass of each pencil.

MASTERMINDERS

16 A milkman delivers milk to 300 houses:

62 houses have 4 bottles,

45 houses have 3 bottles,

112 houses have 2 bottles, and

81 houses have 1 bottle.

He starts the round with 45 crates on his float, each of which contains 16 bottles. How many full crates will he have left at the end of the round?

17 The distance from London to Fishguard is 400 km. Find the distance between each pair of adjacent places on the map, given that:

- Gloucester is the same distance from Carmarthen as it is from Uxbridge.
- This distance is twice the distance from Carmarthen to Fishguard.
- The distance from Carmarthen to Fishguard is three times the distance from London to Uxbridge.

18 To carry loaves from his van, a baker has a delivery tray which measures 60 cm by 45 cm.

The large loaves measure 30 cm by 20 cm and the small loaves 20 cm by 15 cm.

During a delivery round he makes three stops in one street and delivers the following loaves:

1st stop: 3 of each

2nd stop: 2 large and 5 small

3rd stop: 1 large and 7 small

At each stop it is possible to pack all the loaves onto his tray so that they fill it exactly. Draw diagrams which show how this is done for each of the three cases.

19 A locomotive hauls a train from London to Edinburgh. It consumes five litres of diesel for every kilometre that it travels.

a Find the amount of diesel it consumes between London and Newcastle if the distance is 429 km.

b Find the distance from Newcastle on to Edinburgh if it consumes 990 litres of diesel while travelling between these two stations.

c Find the amount of diesel left in the fuel tank when the train reaches Edinburgh if it contained 5000 litres of diesel when the train left London.

d After arrival in Edinburgh it is intended to use the locomotive and its train for making two return journeys to Dundee. If the distance on to Dundee is 93 km, find how many litres of diesel will be left in the tank when the train finally returns to Edinburgh.

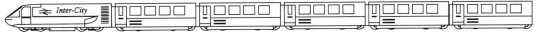

5

___ 1.2 Directed numbers

In this section we use the measurement of temperature to demonstrate how 'directed numbers' can be added and subtracted. Later in the course you will use other types of directed number. (Negative 'directed numbers' are sometimes called 'negative numbers'.)

■ *EXAMPLE 1*

1   This thermometer shows a temperature of $3\,°C$. The temperature drops by $4\,°C$. What is the new temperature?

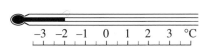

The new temperature is $3\,°C - 4\,°C = -1\,°C$.

2   On another occasion the thermometer shows a temperature of $-2\,°C$. The temperature now rises by $5\,°C$. What is the new temperature?

The new temperature is $-2\,°C + 5\,°C = 3\,°C$.

___ Exercise 3

Make a large drawing of a thermometer showing temperatures from $-10\,°C$ to $10\,°C$. Copy the following table. Use your drawing to help complete it. The first two lines give the answers to parts 1 and 2 of the Example.

	Temperature shown (°C)	Temperature change (°C)	Working	New temp. (°C)
1	3	− 4	3 − 4 = − 1	− 1
2	− 2	+ 5	− 2 + 5 = 3	3
3	2	− 6		
4	− 1	− 6		
5	− 9	+ 6		
6	− 4	+ 4		
7	5	− 5		
8	6			− 6
9	− 5			+ 1
10	− 2			− 9
11	− 7			+ 9
12		− 9		− 5
13		+ 7		+ 2
14		− 3		− 8
15		− 18		− 10

MASTERMINDERS

16   Add:
   a $4.8\,°C$ to $-1.7\,°C$
   b $-4.8\,°C$ to $1.7\,°C$

17   Subtract:
   a $4.8\,°C$ from $-1.7\,°C$
   b $-4.8\,°C$ from $1.7\,°C$

— 1.3 Fractions

— *Activity 1*

This circle is divided into **four** equal parts. **One** of the parts is shaded. (A 'fraction chart' can be any shape but must be divided into equal parts.)

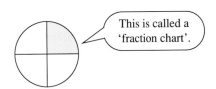

This is called a 'fraction chart'.

The shaded part represents $\frac{1}{4}$ of the whole circle.

The unshaded part represents $\frac{3}{4}$ of the whole circle.

Notice that $\frac{1}{4} + \frac{3}{4} = \frac{4}{4} = 1$.

1 Copy fraction charts **a** to **d**. In each case, write down the fraction which is (i) shaded (ii) unshaded. For each chart add together your answers to (i) and (ii) and comment on the results.

a   **b**   **c**   **d**

2 Draw fraction charts of any shape to help illustrate each of these fractions:
$$\frac{1}{8}, \quad \frac{1}{10}, \quad \frac{3}{8}, \quad \frac{5}{6}, \quad \frac{1}{5}, \quad \frac{6}{7}$$

NOTE

- The number on the top of the fraction is called the 'numerator'.
- The number on the bottom is called the 'denominator'.

The shaded parts of this fraction chart represent two eighths ($\frac{2}{8}$) of the whole diagram.

We can simplify this fraction by dividing both the numerator and the denominator by two.

$$\frac{2}{8} = \frac{1}{4}$$

3 Copy the fraction charts **a** and **b**. In each case, write down what fraction is shaded. If possible, simplify your answers.

a   **b**

■ *EXAMPLE 1*

Reduce each of the following fractions to its lowest terms. Find which fraction has a different value from the other two.

a $\frac{16}{60}$ **b** $\frac{36}{150}$ **c** $\frac{28}{105}$

a $\frac{16}{60} \xrightarrow{\div 2} = \frac{8}{30} \xrightarrow{\div 2} = \frac{4}{15}$ **b** $\frac{36}{150} \xrightarrow{\div 2} = \frac{18}{75} \xrightarrow{\div 3} = \frac{6}{25}$ **c** $\frac{28}{105} \xrightarrow{\div 7} = \frac{4}{15}$

Therefore **b** has a different value from the other two.

> *REMEMBER*
>
> To reduce a fraction to its lowest terms, the **same** number must be divided into the numerator and into the denominator.

___ Exercise 4

For each question, reduce each fraction to its lowest terms and find which, of **a**, **b** and **c**, has a different value from the other two.

1 a $\frac{6}{8}$ **b** $\frac{20}{24}$ **c** $\frac{9}{12}$

2 a $\frac{18}{30}$ **b** $\frac{16}{24}$ **c** $\frac{24}{36}$

3 a $\frac{40}{48}$ **b** $\frac{35}{40}$ **c** $\frac{63}{72}$

4 a $\frac{12}{32}$ **b** $\frac{18}{48}$ **c** $\frac{24}{60}$

5 a $\frac{27}{90}$ **b** $\frac{25}{75}$ **c** $\frac{15}{50}$

6 a $\frac{15}{90}$ **b** $\frac{10}{75}$ **c** $\frac{8}{60}$

7 a $\frac{21}{36}$ **b** $\frac{40}{64}$ **c** $\frac{60}{96}$

MASTERMINDERS

8 a $\frac{135}{300}$ **b** $\frac{150}{360}$ **c** $\frac{144}{320}$

9 a $\frac{192}{360}$ **b** $\frac{144}{270}$ **c** $\frac{135}{240}$

10 a $\frac{15}{180}$ **b** $\frac{72}{900}$ **c** $\frac{32}{400}$

We can also **multiply** the numerator and the denominator by the same number, without altering the value of the fraction. Look at the following example and try to explain why each fraction in the series of fractions has the same value.

■ *EXAMPLE 2*

Fill in the missing numbers:

a $\quad \dfrac{1}{5} = \dfrac{}{10} = \dfrac{}{25} = \dfrac{}{60} = \dfrac{3}{} = \dfrac{7}{} = \dfrac{15}{}$

b $\quad \dfrac{150}{180} = \dfrac{}{90} = \dfrac{}{30} = \dfrac{}{12} = \dfrac{50}{} = \dfrac{30}{} = \dfrac{5}{}$

The completed series of fractions are as follows:

a $\quad \dfrac{1}{5} = \dfrac{2}{10} = \dfrac{5}{25} = \dfrac{12}{60} = \dfrac{3}{15} = \dfrac{7}{35} = \dfrac{15}{75}$

b $\quad \dfrac{150}{180} = \dfrac{75}{90} = \dfrac{25}{30} = \dfrac{10}{12} = \dfrac{50}{60} = \dfrac{30}{36} = \dfrac{5}{6}$

___ Exercise 5

Copy the following series of fractions and fill in the missing numbers.

1 $\quad \dfrac{1}{6} = \dfrac{}{18} = \dfrac{}{36} = \dfrac{}{48} = \dfrac{5}{} = \dfrac{9}{} = \dfrac{25}{}$

2 $\quad \dfrac{3}{5} = \dfrac{}{30} = \dfrac{}{45} = \dfrac{}{80} = \dfrac{12}{} = \dfrac{21}{} = \dfrac{45}{}$

3 $\quad \dfrac{3}{8} = \dfrac{}{40} = \dfrac{}{120} = \dfrac{}{200} = \dfrac{21}{} = \dfrac{60}{} = \dfrac{375}{}$

4 $\quad \dfrac{5}{12} = \dfrac{}{36} = \dfrac{}{96} = \dfrac{}{180} = \dfrac{25}{} = \dfrac{45}{} = \dfrac{60}{}$

5 $\quad \dfrac{8}{15} = \dfrac{}{60} = \dfrac{}{135} = \dfrac{}{300} = \dfrac{48}{} = \dfrac{56}{} = \dfrac{128}{}$

6 $\quad \dfrac{90}{360} = \dfrac{}{120} = \dfrac{}{72} = \dfrac{}{24} = \dfrac{15}{} = \dfrac{5}{} = \dfrac{1}{}$

7 $\quad \dfrac{160}{240} = \dfrac{}{30} = \dfrac{}{12} = \dfrac{}{48} = \dfrac{40}{} = \dfrac{10}{} = \dfrac{2}{}$

MASTERMINDERS

8 $\quad \dfrac{240}{300} = \dfrac{}{50} = \dfrac{}{20} = \dfrac{}{15} = \dfrac{20}{} = \dfrac{60}{} = \dfrac{4}{}$

9 $\quad \dfrac{600}{960} = \dfrac{150}{} = \dfrac{20}{} = \dfrac{25}{} = \dfrac{}{24} = \dfrac{}{64} = \dfrac{}{8}$

10 $\quad \dfrac{1050}{1800} = \dfrac{21}{} = \dfrac{14}{} = \dfrac{175}{} = \dfrac{}{60} = \dfrac{}{72} = \dfrac{}{12}$

___ Addition and subtraction

In order to add or subtract fractions they must be of the same type, that is, each must have the same denominator.

If the denominators are different, the first step is to make them the same ('like terms').

■ *EXAMPLE 3*
Work out:

a $\frac{3}{8} + \frac{5}{16}$ 　　　　　　　**b** $\frac{3}{4} - \frac{1}{5}$ 　　　　　　　**c** $1 - \frac{3}{11}$

The answers are as follows:

a $\dfrac{3}{8} + \dfrac{5}{16} = \dfrac{6}{16} + \dfrac{5}{16} = \dfrac{11}{16}$ 　　**b** $\dfrac{3}{4} - \dfrac{1}{5} = \dfrac{15}{20} - \dfrac{4}{20} = \dfrac{11}{20}$ 　　**c** $1 - \dfrac{3}{11} = \dfrac{11}{11} - \dfrac{3}{11} = \dfrac{8}{11}$

___ *REMEMBER*

> To add or subtract fractions: they must have the same denominators (they must be 'like terms').

___ Exercise 6

For each of the following, find which, of **a**, **b** and **c**, has a different answer from the other two.

1 **a** $\frac{1}{3} + \frac{5}{12}$ 　　　　　**b** $\frac{1}{5} + \frac{11}{20}$ 　　　　　**c** $\frac{1}{10} + \frac{11}{15}$

2 **a** $\frac{1}{4} + \frac{9}{20}$ 　　　　　**b** $\frac{7}{20} + \frac{11}{40}$ 　　　　　**c** $\frac{1}{6} + \frac{8}{15}$

3 **a** $\frac{5}{6} - \frac{7}{30}$ 　　　　　**b** $\frac{11}{15} - \frac{3}{20}$ 　　　　　**c** $\frac{17}{20} - \frac{1}{4}$

4 **a** $1 - \frac{5}{9}$ 　　　　　**b** $\frac{1}{3} + \frac{2}{9}$ 　　　　　**c** $\frac{2}{3} - \frac{1}{9}$

5 **a** $\frac{1}{5} + \frac{1}{4}$ 　　　　　**b** $1 - \frac{11}{20}$ 　　　　　**c** $\frac{3}{5} - \frac{3}{8}$

6 **a** $\frac{1}{2} + \frac{3}{22}$ 　　　　　**b** $\frac{7}{11} - \frac{9}{22}$ 　　　　　**c** $1 - \frac{4}{11}$

7 **a** $\frac{1}{5} + \frac{3}{10} + \frac{9}{20}$ 　　　**b** $\frac{3}{4} + \frac{3}{5} - \frac{1}{2}$ 　　　**c** $\frac{3}{8} + \frac{4}{5} - \frac{9}{40}$

8 **a** $\frac{1}{4} + \frac{3}{20} - \frac{1}{40}$ 　　**b** $\frac{5}{12} + \frac{1}{30} - \frac{3}{40}$ 　　**c** $\frac{9}{20} + \frac{7}{15} - \frac{7}{12}$

MASTERMINDERS

9 **a** $1\frac{3}{5} + 1\frac{1}{10} + 1\frac{2}{15}$ 　　**b** $2\frac{1}{30} + \frac{11}{20} + 1\frac{1}{6}$ 　　**c** $2\frac{1}{4} + 1\frac{1}{20} + \frac{8}{15}$

10 **a** $1\frac{1}{5} + \frac{5}{12} - \frac{11}{30}$ 　　**b** $2\frac{2}{3} + \frac{3}{10} - 1\frac{19}{30}$ 　　**c** $3\frac{5}{6} + \frac{1}{5} - 2\frac{7}{10}$

▬ Multiplication and division

In order to simplify fractions, the numerator and denominator must be divided by the same number. (This process is often called 'cancelling'.)

■*EXAMPLE 4*

Simplify:

a $\frac{30}{51}$ **b** $\frac{2 \times 15}{3 \times 17}$ **c** $\frac{2}{3} \times \frac{15}{17}$

The answers are as follows:

a $\frac{^{10}\cancel{30}}{_{17}\cancel{51}} = \frac{10}{17}$ **b** $\frac{2}{_1\cancel{3}} \times \frac{\cancel{15}^5}{17} = \frac{10}{17}$ **c** $\frac{2 \times \cancel{15}^5}{_1\cancel{3} \times 17} = \frac{10}{17}$

> ▬ *REMEMBER*
>
> To multiply simple fractions: cancel, then multiply out.

In order to divide by a fraction, turn it upsidedown and multiply.
(We know that there are six halves in 3. So, $3 \div \frac{1}{2} = 6$, which can be obtained by $3 \times \frac{2}{1} = 6$.)

■*EXAMPLE 5*

What is $6 \div \frac{1}{3}$? $\quad 6 \left(\div \frac{1}{3} \right) = 6 \left(\times \frac{3}{1} \right) = 18$

becomes

The same method can be applied when both numbers are fractions.

■*EXAMPLE 6*

Find $\frac{3}{14} \div \frac{2}{7}$. $\quad \frac{3}{14} \left(\div \frac{2}{7} \right) = \frac{3}{14} \left(\times \frac{7}{2} \right) = \frac{3}{_2\cancel{14}} \times \frac{\cancel{7}^1}{2} = \frac{3}{4}$

becomes

■*EXAMPLE 7*

What is $\frac{4}{5} \div 3$? $\quad \frac{4}{5} \left(\div 3 \right) = \frac{4}{5} \left(\times \frac{1}{3} \right) = \frac{4}{15}$

becomes

> ▬ *REMEMBER*
>
> To divide by a simple fraction: turn it upsidedown and multiply.

___ Exercise 7

For each of the following, find which, of **a**, **b** and **c**, has a different answer from the other two.

1 **a** $\frac{5}{6} \times \frac{9}{25}$ **b** $\frac{9}{10} \times \frac{8}{15}$ **c** $\frac{3}{8} \times \frac{4}{5}$

2 **a** $\frac{5}{18} \times \frac{8}{25}$ **b** $\frac{16}{27} \times \frac{3}{20}$ **c** $\frac{4}{9} \times \frac{15}{64}$

3 **a** $\frac{2}{3} \div \frac{20}{21}$ **b** $\frac{8}{15} \div \frac{5}{6}$ **c** $\frac{3}{8} \div \frac{15}{28}$

4 **a** $\frac{2}{3} \times \frac{3}{5}$ **b** $\frac{3}{13} \div \frac{9}{26}$ **c** $2 \div 3$

5 **a** $5 \times \frac{3}{5}$ **b** $3 \div \frac{3}{5}$ **c** $\frac{3}{5} \div \frac{3}{25}$

6 **a** $\frac{34}{35} \times \frac{7}{17}$ **b** $\frac{21}{65} \div \frac{7}{13}$ **c** $\frac{57}{60} \times \frac{12}{19}$

7 **a** $\frac{1}{2} \times \frac{15}{16} \times \frac{4}{5}$ **b** $\frac{2}{3} \times \frac{3}{5} \times \frac{9}{10}$ **c** $\frac{5}{6} \times \frac{4}{5} \times \frac{9}{16}$

MASTERMINDERS

8 **a** $1\frac{7}{8} \times \frac{2}{3}$ **b** $1\frac{1}{9} \times 1\frac{1}{8}$ **c** $3\frac{1}{5} \times \frac{5}{12}$

9 **a** $1\frac{1}{20} \div \frac{7}{16}$ **b** $4\frac{4}{5} \div 2\frac{2}{15}$ **c** $12 \div 5\frac{1}{3}$

___ Problem solving

■EXAMPLE 8

There are 4000 books in a library. Five eighths are hardbacks and the rest are paperbacks.
a Draw a fraction chart to show the fractions of each type of book.
b Work out the number of books which are paperbacks.

a If $\frac{5}{8}$ are hardbacks, $\frac{3}{8}$ are paperbacks.

b [W] Number of paperback books

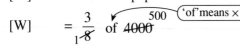

[W] $= \frac{3}{8} \text{ of } 4000$ ('of' means ×)

[A] $= 1500$

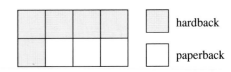

■EXAMPLE 9

Marion cycles 24 miles of a 28-mile journey. What fraction of her journey remains?

[W] Fraction of journey remaining (four miles to go)

[W] $= \frac{4}{28}$

[A] $= \frac{1}{7}$

12

▬ Exercise 8

1 Work out:
   a $\frac{5}{9}$ of 108 m   **b** $\frac{7}{8}$ of 104 kg   **c** $\frac{4}{7}$ of 637 cm
   d $\frac{3}{11}$ of £176   **e** $\frac{12}{13}$ of 169 g   **f** $\frac{3}{19}$ of 152 mm

2 Which is more and by how much?
   a $\frac{3}{5}$ of £4.60   **b** $\frac{4}{7}$ of £4.90

3 Which is less and by how much?
   a $\frac{7}{9}$ of 135 m   **b** $\frac{5}{8}$ of 176 m

4 In a school of 583 pupils, $\frac{5}{11}$ are girls.
   a Draw a fraction chart to illustrate the fractions which are of each sex.
   b How many are boys?

5 Kate tosses a coin 100 times. There are 48 heads.
   What fraction are **a** heads **b** tails?

6 An ordinary die was thrown 150 times. A 'one' appeared 20 times. In what fraction of the throws did a 'one' not appear?

7 A quarter of the pupils in a class live in flats and five eighths live in detached houses. What fraction live neither in flats nor in detached houses?

8 The area of the square is 121 cm².
   What area is **a** shaded **b** unshaded?

9 From a length of wood 60 cm long, a piece 48 cm long is cut off. What fraction remains?

10 The Sears Tower in Chicago is the tallest occupied building in the world and is 1450 feet high.
   How high is the Blackpool Tower if it is $\frac{9}{25}$ of the height of the Sears Tower?

11 There are 5000 books in a school library. Copy and complete the table below.

Type of book	Number of each type of book	Fraction of the total
Fiction	3500	
Reference	1000	
Biography		

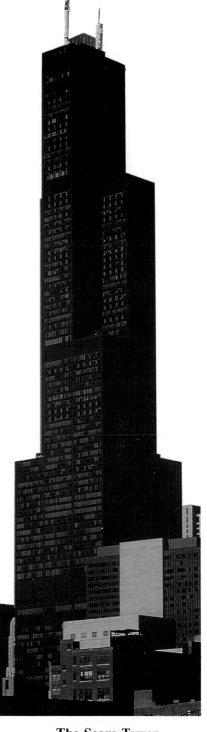

The Sears Tower

12 The diameter of the Earth is 13 000 km. What is the diameter of the Moon if it is seven twenty-fifths of the diameter of the Earth?

13 By the year 2000 it is estimated that there will be about 5 400 000 000 people in the world, of which 1 800 000 000 will live in China. What fraction will live in China?

14 The population of a country is 34 million. What will be the population if it increases by a fifth?

15 A car was bought for £50 000. After a year its value dropped by an eighth. What was it then worth?

16 In 1685 the average wage of a peasant in England was equivalent to 20p a week.
What would be the average wage if it increased by two fifths?

(Engraving by Hogarth.)

MASTERMINDERS

17 A school netball team won ten matches, lost four and drew an eighth of the total played. How many matches were drawn and what fraction did the team win?

18 Seven tenths of the Earth's surface is sea. The surface area which is not sea is 60 million square miles. What is the total surface area of the Earth?

19 Half a pint of alcohol is put into a pint pot which is then filled up with water and mixed. Half a pint of the mixture is poured away and the pot refilled with water and mixed. This operation is repeated twice more. Find what fraction of alcohol there is in the mixture at the end.

20 One way of stating the strength of a wine is to quote the fraction of its volume which is alcohol. What do you do to the strength of a wine if you mix with it half the quantity of a wine twice its strength?

1.4 Decimals

Place value

The place value of each of the digits in the number 5246 is shown in the table.

	Thousands	Hundreds	Tens	Units
Digit	5	2	4	6
Value	5 × 1000 = 5000	2 × 100 = 200	4 × 10 = 40	6 × 1 = 6

Now look carefully at the number 0.319 and the place value of its digits.

To summarize the place values:

	Tenths	Hundredths	Thousandths
Digit	3	1	9
Value	3 × 0.1 or 3 × $\frac{1}{10}$ = $\frac{3}{10}$	1 × 0.01 or 1 × $\frac{1}{100}$ = $\frac{1}{100}$	9 × 0.001 or 9 × $\frac{1}{1000}$ = $\frac{9}{1000}$

thousands hundreds tens units tenths hundredths thousandths

5   2   4   6   .   3   1   9

Exercise 9

In Questions 1 to 30, find the value of the underlined digit, writing it as a fraction if appropriate.

1 3<u>4</u>6	**2** 2<u>9</u>6	**3** <u>7</u>5	**4** 253<u>2</u>	**5** 43<u>2</u>6
6 2<u>7</u>15	**7** <u>9</u>24	**8** <u>9</u>24.5	**9** 9<u>2</u>4.5	**10** 92<u>4</u>.5
11 3<u>7</u>.6	**12** 29.<u>2</u>4	**13** 8.<u>3</u>5	**14** 8.3<u>5</u>	**15** 8.3<u>5</u>2
16 5.<u>7</u>25	**17** 1.8<u>3</u>4	**18** 3.6<u>1</u>8	**19** 9.<u>5</u>4	**20** 2.57<u>3</u>
21 7.2<u>9</u>6	**22** 3.4<u>6</u>2	**23** 8.1<u>8</u>5	**24** 4.9<u>2</u>	**25** 6.73<u>9</u>
26 1.51<u>3</u>	**27** 2.42<u>1</u>	**28** 4.03<u>4</u>	**29** 7.80<u>8</u>	**30** 5.37<u>5</u>

31 Copy this number line:

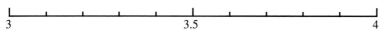

3   3.5   4

On your number line mark the following: 3.1,   3.9,   3.35,   3.75, $3\frac{1}{4}$,   3.62

■ EXAMPLE 1
a   Multiply 0.8 by (i) 10 (ii) 100 and (iii) 1000.
b   Divide 60 by (i) 10 (ii) 100 and (iii) 1000

a   (i) 0.8 × 10 = 8   (ii) 0.8 × 100 = 80   (iii) 0.8 × 1000 = 800
b   (i) 60 ÷ 10 = 6   (ii) 60 ÷ 100 = 0.6   (iii) 60 ÷ 1000 = 0.06

■ *EXAMPLE 2*

Find the missing number in each of the following:

a $2.7 \times ? = 270$

b $4 \div ? = 0.004$. (This question could have been written in another way: $\frac{4}{?} = 0.004$)

a $2.7 \times 100 = 270$. Therefore 100 is the missing number.
b $4 \div 1000 = 0.004$. Therefore 1000 is the missing number.

___ Exercise 10

1 Copy and complete this table:

	n	$n \times 10$	$n \times 100$	$n \times 1000$
a	420			
b	25			
c	21.6			
d		12.5		
e			6.4	
f				39

2 Copy and complete this table:

	n	$n \div 10$	$n \div 100$	$n \div 1000$
a	500			
b	78			
c	51.3			
d		0.258		
e			0.007	
f				0.000 08

3 Find the missing number:
  a $76 \times ? = 760$ **b** $1350 = ? \times 13.5$ **c** $6.25 \times ? = 6250$ **d** $3600 = ? \times 3.6$
  e $0.312 \times ? = 312$ **f** $200 = ? \times 0.2$ **g** $9.6 = ? \times 0.096$ **h** $0.002\,4 \times ? = 0.24$

4 Find the missing number:
  a $546 \div ? = 54.6$ **b** $\frac{95}{?} = 9.5$ **c** $28 \div ? = 0.028$ **d** $\frac{53.2}{?} = 5.32$
  e $0.225 = 2.25 \div ?$ **f** $\frac{7.32}{?} = 0.073\,2$ **g** $0.009 = 0.9 \div ?$ **h** $0.000\,16 = \frac{0.16}{?}$

5 Write down a number between:
  a 3.5 and 3.9   **b** 3.5 and 3.52   **c** 11.03 and 11.08   **d** 5.7 and 5.8
  e 8.06 and 8.07   **f** 0.6 and 0.62   **g** 0.03 and 0.031   **h** 12 and 12.01

6 Which of the two numbers is larger?
  a 0.3 or 0.4   **b** 0.4 or 0.38   **c** 0.7 or 0.608   **d** 0.04 or 0.08
  e 0.09 or 0.123   **f** 0.089 or 0.080 9   **g** 0.002 or 0.001 2   **h** 0.000 4 or 0.004 1

MASTERMINDER

7 Find the missing number:

   a $\frac{4.6}{?} = 460$ **b** $602 \times ? = 6.02$ **c** $0.78 \div ? = 0.01$ **d** $100 = \frac{36}{?}$

   e $40 = 3.2 \div ?$ **f** $3060 \times ? = 91.8$ **g** $0.002 = ? \div 40.3$

   Can you find a rule, apart from guess-work, to help work out these questions?

Addition and subtraction

In order to add or subtract decimal quantities, we must arrange the digits so that the decimal points are lined up with each other. This makes sure that tenths are added to tenths, hundredths are added to hundredths, etc.

■ *EXAMPLE 3*

Work out: **a** $39.12 + 0.026 + 3$ **b** $43.1 - 9.256$

```
a     39.120              b      43.100
       0.026                   -  9.256
    +  3.000                     33.844
      42.146
```

REMEMBER

When adding or subtracting decimal quantities: line up the decimal points.

Exercise 11

For each of the following, find which, of **a**, **b** and **c**, has a different answer from the other two.

   1   **a** $37.83 + 19.25 + 24.67$ **b** $28.44 + 47.03 + 6.18$ **c** $18.39 + 33.56 + 29.8$

   2   **a** $20.32 + 17.6 + 7.4$ **b** $27.39 + 9.83 + 8.1$ **c** $7.2 + 36.75 + 2.37$

   3   **a** $29.96 + 7.03 + 0.51$ **b** $12.45 + 11.6 + 13$ **c** $14.83 + 20 + 2.67$

   4   **a** $7.2 + 3 + 17.8$ **b** $25.39 + 0.4 + 2.21$ **c** $11.6 + 16.54 + 0.86$

   5   **a** $10.32 + 11 + 0.68$ **b** $6 + 14.47 + 0.53$ **c** $8.071 + 12.28 + 0.649$

   6   **a** $1.004 + 3.5 + 5$ **b** $7.46 + 0.894 + 0.7$ **c** $2.5 + 6.934 + 0.07$

   7   **a** $58.19 - 42.83$ **b** $41.06 - 25.8$ **c** $72.9 - 57.54$

   8   **a** $43.03 - 9.43$ **b** $112.4 - 79.8$ **c** $129 - 96.4$

   9   **a** $102.07 - 73.35$ **b** $37.3 - 8.58$ **c** $95 - 67.18$

   10   **a** $11.39 - 7.682$ **b** $12.7 - 9.622$ **c** $10 - 6.292$

MASTERMINDERS

11 a $12.1 + 13.378 - 19.199$ **b** $6.874 + 0.926 - 1.511$ **c** $2.93 + 4.195 - 0.836$

12 a $47 + 59.34 - 28.99$ **b** $86.5 + 0.79 - 9.76$ **c** $120.4 + 58.93 - 101.8$

___ Multiplication

In order to multiply two decimal quantities together, first find the product ignoring the decimal points. Then place the decimal point in the product. Example 4 shows how this is done.

■ *EXAMPLE 4*

Work out 3.265×1.4.

Note: there is a total of 4 digits after the decimal points.

$$3.265 \times 1.4$$
$$= 4.5710$$

Note: there is also a total of 4 digits after the decimal point in the answer.

	3265
	14
(10×3265)	32650
(4×3265)	13060
	45710

___ Exercise 12

For each of the following, find which, of **a**, **b** and **c**, has a different answer from the other two.

1 a 11.4×7 **b** 9.85×8 **c** 6.65×12

2 a 4.225×8 **b** 14×2.4 **c** 224×0.15

3 a 6.2×2.8 **b** 3.88×4.5 **c** 48.5×0.36

4 a 172.8×0.75 **b** 231.25×0.56 **c** 10.125×12.8

5 a 14.25×0.32 **b** 0.608×7.5 **c** 0.425×11.2

6 a 1.775×0.48 **b** 61×0.014 **c** 35.5×0.024

7 a 10.875×0.08 **b** 11.2×0.075 **c** 240×0.0035

8 a 16.8×0.0025 **b** 0.375×0.12 **c** $0.018\,75 \times 2.24$

MASTERMINDERS

9 a $1.024 \times 0.75 \times 0.125$ **b** $18.75 \times 0.08 \times 0.064$ **c** $0.4375 \times 0.56 \times 0.4$

10 a $0.625 \times 0.64 \times 0.95$ **b** $1.92 \times 0.015 \times 12.5$ **c** $9.375 \times 24 \times 0.0016$

__ Division

> **REMEMBER**
>
> If two numbers are written $\frac{28}{3}$, it means $28 \div 3$.

■ *EXAMPLE 5*

Divide 396.5 by 13.

This question could have been written in two other ways:

'Work out $396.5 \div 13$' or 'Work out $\frac{396.5}{13}$'.

$396.5 \div 13$

$= 30.5$

Line up the decimal points.

$$
\begin{array}{r}
30.5 \\
13\overline{\smash{\big)}\,396.5} \\
\underline{39} \quad\quad (3 \times 13) \\
65 \\
\underline{65} \quad (5 \times 13) \\
00
\end{array}
$$

__ Exercise 13

For each of the following find which, of **a**, **b** and **c**, has a different answer from the other two.

1 a $28.75 \div 5$ **b** $52.65 \div 9$ **c** $120.75 \div 21$

2 a $292.25 \div 35$ **b** $49.5 \div 6$ **c** $66.8 \div 8$

3 a $271.7 \div 22$ **b** $294 \div 24$ **c** $247 \div 20$

4 a $11.41 \div 7$ **b** $14.67 \div 9$ **c** $19.68 \div 12$

5 a $258.72 \div 11$ **b** $330.68 \div 14$ **c** $117.6 \div 5$

6 a $3.93 \div 12$ **b** $4.05 \div 12$ **c** $4.725 \div 14$

7 a $\frac{13.59}{18}$ **b** $\frac{12.08}{16}$ **c** $\frac{11.34}{15}$

8 a $\frac{0.6954}{19}$ **b** $\frac{0.4745}{13}$ **c** $\frac{0.6222}{17}$

MASTERMINDERS

9 a $\frac{3.2 \times 9.45}{0.36}$ **b** $\frac{21.5 \times 3.4}{0.85}$ **c** $\frac{30.24 \times 12.5}{4.5}$

10 a $\frac{2.625 \times 3.6}{0.14}$ **b** $\frac{16.25 \times 1.04}{0.25}$ **c** $\frac{216 \times 0.225}{0.72}$

1.5 The calculator

REMEMBER

1 Carry out multiplication and division before addition and subtraction.

2 Check your answer against a rough estimate.

■ *EXAMPLE 1*

Work out the following. Check each answer with a rough estimate.

a $235 + 7.9 - 3.5$ **b** 38×3.95 **c** $\frac{165.3}{9.5}$ **d** $\frac{14.945}{4.9} - 6.38$

Before doing any calculation you must clear your calculator by pressing the **AC** button.

a **AC** 235 **+** 7.9 **−** 3.5 **=** 239.4 (Rough estimate $200 + 8 - 3 = 205$)

b **AC** 38 **×** 3.95 **=** 150.1 (Rough estimate $40 \times 4 = 160$)

c **AC** 165.3 **÷** 9.5 **=** 17.4 (Rough estimate $200 \div 10 = 20$)

d **AC** 14.945 **÷** 4.9 **−** 6.38 **=** −3.33 (Rough estimate $15 \div 5 - 6 = 3 - 6 = -3$)

Exercise 14

Answer the following using your calculator. Add a rough estimate in brackets.

1 $23.5 + 79$ **2** $56.9 + 12.9$ **3** $345 - 17.9$ **4** $6702 - 289$

5 $36.7 - 54.9$ **6** $0.927 - 0.74$ **7** 24×19.5 **8** 56.5×8.2

9 $45.6 \div 9.5$ **10** $98 \div 0.35$ **11** $\frac{20.3}{2.9}$ **12** $\frac{323.9}{41}$

13 $\frac{224}{3.5}$ **14** $\frac{39.9}{4.2}$ **15** $\frac{74.1}{9.5} + 49$ **16** $\frac{28.5}{3.8} - 14.75$

17 $\frac{266}{76} \times 1.2$ **18** $\frac{84}{3.5} \div 0.6$ **19** $\frac{5}{8} \times 6312$ **20** $\frac{4}{7} \times 553$

21 $\frac{3}{13} \times 101.4$ **22** $\frac{2}{17} \times 8.16$ **23** $\frac{4}{7}$ of 441 **24** $\frac{1}{9}$ of 71.01

MASTERMINDERS

25 $\frac{48.6 + 562.4}{0.94}$ **26** $\frac{23.87 - 7.26}{3.02}$ **27** $\frac{5}{8} - 23.9$ **28** $32 \div \frac{0.04}{1.8}$

29 $\frac{7}{24} - \frac{1}{6}$ **30** $\frac{37.5 \times 11.2}{156 + 54}$ **31** $\frac{1.26 \times 5.6}{0.16 \times 1.4}$ **32** $\frac{0.49 \times 0.84}{8.75 - 6.79}$

Rounding

The answers to many calculations often do not work out exactly. For example, when using your calculator to divide 67 by 0.71 the answer displayed (using an 8-digit calculator) is:

94.366 197

This is not the exact answer. It is only the answer written using the first 8 digits. It is often sensible to write an answer to the nearest 100, the nearest 10, etc.
Look carefully at these number-line diagrams on the right:

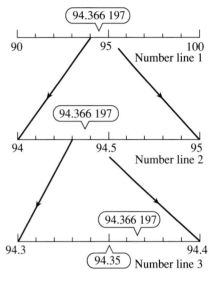

This table summarizes the conclusions:

Number line	94.366 197 is:
1	nearer to 90 than to 100
2	nearer to 94 than to 95
3	nearer to 94.4 than to 94.3

■ EXAMPLE 2

Copy this number line: 9.2   9.3

a Mark the position of 9.27.
b Write 9.27 to the nearest tenth.

a

b 9.27 is nearer to 9.3 than to 9.2. Therefore 9.27 = 9.3 to the nearest tenth.

Exercise 15

1 Copy the number line.

        4.7   4.8

  a Mark the position of (i) 4.76 (ii) 4.73 (iii) 4.778.
  b Write each of the numbers to the nearest tenth.

2 Copy the number line.

        2.8   2.9

  a Mark the position of (i) 2.82 (ii) 2.86 (iii) 2.856.
  b Write each of the numbers to the nearest tenth.

3 Copy the number line.

        0.9   1.0

  a Mark the position of (i) 0.98 (ii) 0.94 (iii) 0.9501.
  b Write each of the numbers to the nearest tenth.

For Questions 4 to 13, round each number to **a** the nearest hundred, **b** the nearest ten, **c** the nearest whole number, **d** the nearest tenth. Put your answers into a table.

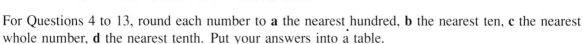

  4 263.51   **5** 678.23   **6** 178.802   **7** 905.86   **8** 1 234.56
  9 4 509.691 7   **10** 12 893.079   **11** 1 590.560 9   **12** 87 001.099   **13** 45 454.545

___ Problem solving

As before, you should solve problems in three stages. First, write down in words what you are trying to find [W]; second, show your working [W]; and third, use your calculator to work out the answer (including the correct units) [A].

> _REMEMBER_
>
> [W]   Words
> [W]   Working
> [A]   Answer (with units)

■ _EXAMPLE 3_

A householder pays 6.6p for each unit of electricity. A unit of electricity from a torch battery costs £99. How many times more expensive is it to use electricity from a battery rather than from an electric socket in your home?

[W]   The number of times a battery is more expensive is

[W] $\dfrac{9900}{6.6}$ (Change £99 to pence.)

[A]   = 1500

> Approximately equal to

Therefore a battery is 1500 times more expensive. (Rough estimate: $10\,000 \div 7 \approx 1400$)

■ _EXAMPLE 4_

Investigate the following facts:

A BAC 111 is 32.16 m long.   A Boeing 747 is 70.66 m long.

Here are two ways of comparing these figures.

1   [W]   The Boeing is longer than the BAC 111 by

   [W] $\dfrac{70.66}{32.16}$ times

   [A] ≈ 2.2 (That is, the Boeing is just over twice as long.)

2   [W]   The Boeing is longer than the BAC 111 by

   [W] $70.66 - 32.16$ metres

   [A]   = 38.5 metres   (That is, the Boeing is nearly 40 metres longer.)

Discuss which you think gives a better comparison.

___ *Activity 2* 📱

1 Measure either your best long jump into a sand pit or your best standing long jump.
2 Compare it with the following world records:

Kangaroo: 12.80 m   Frog: 5.35 m   Woman: 7.09 m   Man 8.95 m

___ **Exercise 16**

1 📱 Five sevenths of a population is under 25 years of age. If the size of the population is 48 909, how many people are over 25 years of age?

2 📱 Three thirteenths of the area of a country is cultivated. If the total area of the country is 807 131 square miles, what area is not cultivated?

3 📱 The women's 100 m world record is 10.49 s. If this is about 0.94 times slower than the men's record, what do you think the men's record is (to the nearest tenth of a second)?

4 📱 The men's 1500 m world record is 3 min 29.46 s. If this is about 1.11 times faster than the women's record, what do you think the women's record is (to the nearest tenth of a second)?

5 📱 In 1910 the deepest mine in the world was the Dolcoath tin mine in Cornwall. It was 3596 feet deep. Compare this with the Telecom Tower in London which is 620 feet high.

6 📱 Here are two world records:

Brick
throwing:
44.54 m

Flying-ring
throwing:
383.13 m

How many times further is the flying-ring-throwing record than the brick-throwing record?

7 📱 The area of the (former) USSR was about 8 650 000 square miles. What is the area of the UK if it is 92 times smaller? Give your answer to the nearest 1000 square miles.
Explain why this means that the USSR was about 92 times larger than the UK.

8 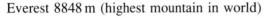 **Investigate** these heights:

Everest 8848 m (highest mountain in world)   Scafell Pike 978 m (highest mountain in England)

9 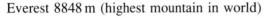 **Investigate** these figures:

Date	Tax on petrol	Cost of 1 gallon
1912	3p	7p
1991	130p	220p

10 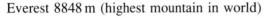 The distance around the Earth's equator is 21 600 nautical miles or 40 000 km. Express 1 km as a fraction of a nautical mile. Convert this fraction to a decimal.
   a Convert the following distances to nautical miles:
      (i) Liverpool to New York, 4800 km   (ii) Liverpool to Montevideo, 11 000 km
      (iii) Southampton to Gibraltar, 2250 km
   b Convert the following distances to kilometres:
      (i) Hull to Rotterdam, 189 nautical miles   (ii) London to Havana, 4050 nautical miles
      (iii) Southampton to Cowes, $13\frac{1}{2}$ nautical miles

11 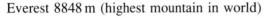 A 60-litre beer cask contains enough beer to fill 125 glasses which are all the same size.
   a Find the capacity of each glass.
   b Find the quantity of beer in a party can, which fills 25 glasses.
   c Find the price charged for a glass of beer by a hotel manager if he takes £67.50 from selling a 60-litre cask.
   d Find the price the hotel manager charges for a party can (if he charges at the same rate).

12 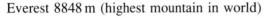 This gate is made from five pieces of wood 0.15 m wide.
   a Find the total length of wood required for making the gate.
   b If the wood is only sold in one – or two – metre lengths, find the length of wood that is wasted.
   c Find the width of the two equal vertical gaps.
   d Find the width of the gap between the two horizontal pieces of wood.
   e The wood weighs $1\frac{1}{2}$ kg per metre length. If each hinge weighs 0.08 kg and the handle weighs 0.26 kg, find the total weight of the gate.

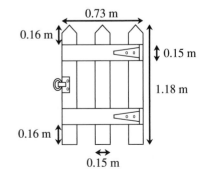

13 Short Street is 63 m long and on both sides of the roadway there are six terraced houses which are all the same width.
A pavement of width 3.15 m runs the full length of both sides of the street and extends around the end corners into the two adjacent streets.

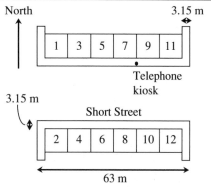

a Find the width of each house.

b Find the distance from the western end of the street to the telephone kiosk, expressed as a fraction of the length of the street.

c Find the number of kerb blocks which line the two pavements if each block is of length 0.84 m.

d Find the number of street lights along the two pavements if they are 18.9 m apart and there is a street light in line with each of the four terrace ends.

MASTERMINDERS

14

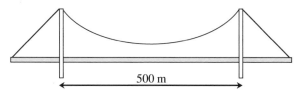

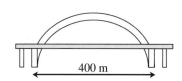

Find the missing numbers in:

a $400 \times ? = 500$

b $500 \times ? = 400$

Explain the meaning of your two answers in relation to the diagram.

15 The table shows the average distance between the Sun and the planets:

Planet	Average distance from Sun (million km)
Mercury	58
Venus	108
Earth	150
Mars	228
Jupiter	778
Saturn	1427
Uranus	2870
Neptune	4497
Pluto	5950

a Compare each of the distances with the distance the Earth is from the Sun.
Illustrate your answers with a suitable diagram.

b **Investigate** this diagram:

Sun   Earth   Nearest star

39 700 000 000 000 km

Revision Exercise 1A

Calculators are **not** allowed for Questions 1 to 10.

1 Work out: **a** $16.9 + 4.87$ **b** $103.7 - 9.8$ **c** 34×1.6 **d** $38.5 \div 11$

2 James bought a secondhand lawnmower for £168. In doing it up he spent £47 on spare parts. He sold it for £270.
  a How much did he spend altogether on the lawnmower?
  b How much profit did he make?

3 A thermometer shows a temperature of $-3\,°C$. If the temperature increases by $7\,°C$, what temperature will be shown on the thermometer?

4 Reduce $\frac{15}{40}$ to its lowest terms.

5 Copy and complete: $\frac{1}{6} = \frac{?}{24}$.

6 Work out: **a** $\frac{1}{3} + \frac{1}{4}$ **b** $1 - \frac{1}{6}$ **c** $\frac{2}{3} \times \frac{1}{4}$ **d** $\frac{2}{21} \div \frac{1}{3}$

7 Work out $\frac{3}{5}$ of £120.

8 In a school of 284 pupils, $\frac{3}{4}$ are boys. How many are girls?

9 Multiply 0.4 by 100.

10 How many times does 0.3 divide into 30?

11 ▦ Work out: **a** 28×0.075 **b** $5.32 \div 5.6$ **c** $\frac{4}{7}$ of 644 **d** $\frac{54.3 + 26.21}{9.7}$

12 ▦ Work out $6.83 - 0.75 + 3.68$ to the nearest tenth.

Revision Exercise 1B

Calculators are **not** allowed for Questions 1 to 10.

1 Work out : **a** $0.78 + 0.078$ **b** $0.78 - 0.078$ **c** 6.8×0.59 **d** $1.444 \div 19$

2 A bottle has a mass of 260 grams when empty. When it is full of water its mass is 630 grams. Find its mass when it is half full.

3 Subtract $8\,°C$ from $-13\,°C$.

4 Reduce $\frac{42}{98}$ to its lowest terms.

5 Copy and complete: $\frac{7.2}{14} = \frac{3.6}{?}$.

6 Work out: **a** $\frac{2}{3} + \frac{1}{8}$ **b** $\frac{4}{11} \div 2$ **c** $\frac{6}{13} \times \frac{26}{27}$ **d** $\frac{6}{17} \div \frac{3}{68}$

7 Jill drives 45 km of a 63 km journey. What fraction remains?

8 What is $\frac{3}{8}$ of £2.64 in pence?

9 Write down a number between 0.4 and 0.3.

10 Find the missing number: $45 = \frac{0.45}{?}$.

11 ▦ Work out to the nearest tenth: **a** $\frac{8.9}{3.6}$ **b** $3.98 - 4.763$ **c** $\frac{7}{13}$ of 98 **d** $\frac{3}{7} \div 7.74$

12 ▦ A Vickers machine gun fires 550 rounds per minute. It was once test-fired nonstop for a week. How many rounds were fired?

13 ▦ The women's 800 m world record is 1 minute 53.28 seconds. If this is about 0.9 times slower than the men's record, what do you think the men's record is (to the nearest tenth of a second)?

___ Basics Test 1

A Calculator

    1 35.23 + 27.27   **2** 9.271 + 4.136 + 4.593

    3 4.5 − 2.125   **4** 53.4 × 1.5

    5 53.4 ÷ 1.5   **6** 48 ÷ 125

B Paper and pencil

    7 36 × 25   **8** 9977 ÷ 11

    9 325 + 76 + 99   **10** 850 − 265

    11 $\frac{3}{5} + \frac{1}{6}$ **12** $\frac{3}{5} \times \frac{1}{6}$

    13 1.45 × 0.8   **14** 728 ÷ 13

    15 What is three sevenths of 14.35?

C Mental

Ten questions will be read out to you.

(Remember: for these questions, you must **not** do any working on paper, only write down the answer.)

___ Puzzlers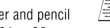

1 The head of a fish is 12 cm long, and the tail is as long as the head plus half the body. The body is as long as the head and tail together. How long is the fish?

2 This puzzle uses matches to make squares in a number of different ways. For example, if eight matches are arranged so as to make two squares as shown in Figure 1, how many squares are made if four matches are moved to the position shown in Figure 2?

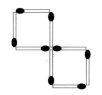

                       Figure 1   **Figure 2**

Now arrange twelve matches as shown in Figure 3. Starting from this layout, make up the four sets of squares as described in the table. Make a drawing of each. (Remember, all the twelve matches have to be used.)

Figure 3

	Number of matches to be moved	Number of squares to be made	Size of new squares
a	3	3	Same
b	4	3	Same
c	2	7	Different
d	4	10	Different

Coursework: Paper folding

This Coursework explores an interesting puzzle made by folding and cutting paper.

1   Take a piece of paper and carefully cut it to make a strip exactly 12 cm wide. Without doing any more measuring, see if you can make a square with a side length of 12 cm. Draw one or more diagrams to show how you have done it.

Figure 1   **Figure 2**

2   Now carefully fold your paper square along each of the broken lines shown in Figure 1.
   a Make a very accurate **full-size** drawing of your paper square, showing folds as broken lines.
   b (i) Explain why the area of your paper square is 144 cm^2.
      (ii) Explain why the area of one of the smallest triangles is $\frac{1}{16}$ of the area of the whole square.
   c Write down the area of one of the smallest triangles.

3   Now turn over your paper square and carefully draw the lines shown in Figure 2. Label each of the five regions. Make a neat **full-size** drawing of Figure 2.

4   The region marked I has the same area as two small triangles. Explain why its area is 18 cm^2. Work out the areas of the other four regions. Copy and complete this table showing your results.

Region	Number of small triangles	Fraction of whole square	Area (cm^2)
I	2	2/16	18
II			
III			
IV			
V			

5   Cut out the five regions drawn on your paper square and from another piece of paper cut out another triangle exactly like the one marked I.
   a Fit all six pieces together to make another large square. Draw a diagram of it.
   b Work out the total area of the square you have just made.

6   Without using the piece marked V, fit together the other five pieces to make yet another square. Draw a diagram to show how you have done it. Work out its area. Comment on your answer.

EXTENSION

7   Using some or all of the six pieces, try to make the patterns shown below. Draw separate diagrams to show how you have done it. Work out the area of each. (Use all six pieces for **a**.)

a   **b**   **c**   **d**

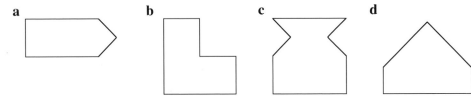

2 GRAPHS

2.1 Grid references

The grid on a map enables us to identify places. On the map of West Cornwall, the town of Penzance is identified by the 6-figure grid reference (130140) and the town of Helston by the grid reference (165135). Notice that the 'Easting' is always written before the 'Northing'.

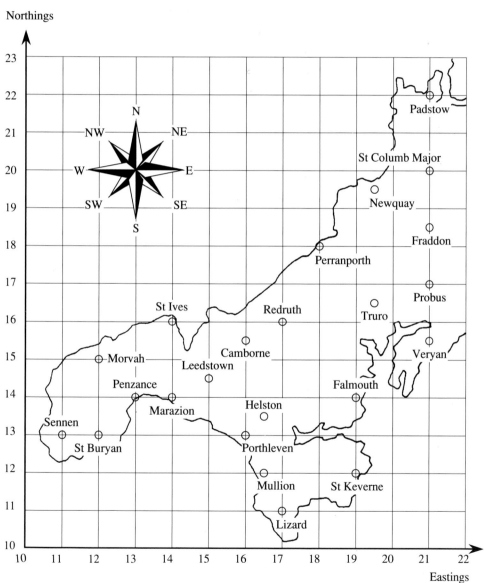

___ Exercise 17

For this Exercise use the map of West Cornwall on the previous page.

1   Write down the grid reference of each of the following places:
   a St Ives   **b** Marazion
   c Lizard   **d** Redruth
   e St Keverne   **f** Falmouth
   g Probus   **h** Leedstown

2   Name the places with these grid references:
   a (120130)   **b** (120150)
   c (160130)   **d** (160155)
   e (180180)   **f** (210185)
   g (210200)   **h** (195165)

3   One centimetre on the map represents five kilometres on the land. Find the direct distance between each of the following pairs of places by measuring the distance on the map.
   a Penzance and Marazion   **b** Penzance and Falmouth
   c Penzance and Lizard   **d** Penzance and St Columb Major
   e St Ives and Marazion   **f** St Ives and St Columb Major
   g Lizard and Redruth   **h** Perranporth and Padstow

4   There is a shipwreck at (100230). Which is the nearest place to it on the map and how far is it from this place to the wreck?

5   A boat is sinking at (140190) but the only available helicopter is at Falmouth. How far does the helicopter have to fly?

6   **a** There is another ship in distress at (110200). How far does a lifeboat from St Ives have to sail in order to reach it?
   b If the lifeboat in **a** sails to (170200) by mistake and then from there to (110200), how far will it have sailed?

MASTERMINDERS

7   A ship sails from Penzance to Falmouth; it sails only in any one of the eight directions shown on the map and only changes direction at points where two grid lines cross. Find its shortest route.

8   A helicopter pilot has to fly from Sennen to Padstow, but there are only two routes which he can follow:

   First route:
   Sennen to (110170), (110170) to (160220), and (160220) to Padstow.
   Second route:
   Sennen to (110160), (110160) to (190220), and (190220) to Padstow.

   If he chooses the shorter route, the flight will last one hour. How long will the flight take if he chooses the longer route?

__ 2.2 Scales

A scale is a length used to measure a quantity. Look at the examples below.

■ *EXAMPLE 1*
The diagram shows a scale of 1 cm to 10 km/h.
What is the speed?

kilometres per hour

The speed is 64 km/h.

■ *EXAMPLE 2*
The diagram shows a clinical thermometer. The scale used is 2 cm to 1 °C or 2 mm to 0.1°C. What is the temperature?

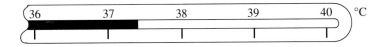

The temperature shown is 37.4 °C.

■ *EXAMPLE 3*
On graph paper use a scale of 1 cm to £10 to draw a line from £0 to £60. Mark carefully with an arrow each of these points: **a** £12 **b** £34 **c** £58

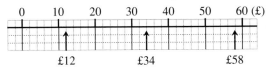

__ *Activity 3*

1 For each of Scales A to C, find: **a** the size of the smallest scale division
b the position of each of the points shown.

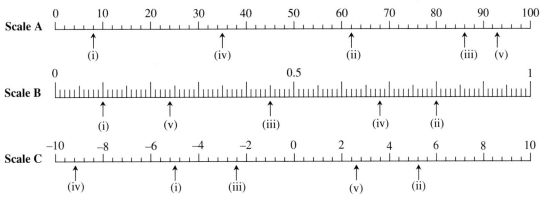

31

2   Using Scale D, find:
    a The size of the smallest scale division.
    b The length of each of the lines shown.

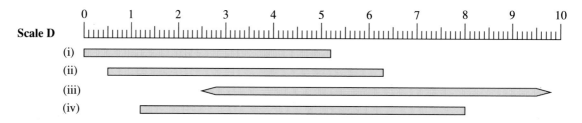

3   Using Scale E, find the position of each of the points shown, to the nearest whole number.

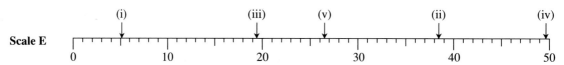

—— Exercise 18

1   On graph paper, use a scale of 2 cm to $10 to draw a line from $0 to $60. Mark each of these points with an arrow:
    a $5   **b** $51   **c** $26   **d** $19   **e** $33   **f** $48
    Measure the distance in millimetres from each of these points to the $0 point.

2   On graph paper, use a scale of 2 cm to 5 francs (Fr) to draw a line from Fr 0 to Fr 30. Mark each of these points with an arrow:
    a Fr 11   **b** Fr 29   **c** Fr 22   **d** Fr 4   **e** Fr $7\frac{1}{2}$ **f** Fr $17\frac{1}{2}$
    Measure the distance in millimetres from each of these points to the Fr 0 point.

3   On graph paper, use a scale of 12 cm to 1 hour to draw a line from 10:00 am to 11:00 am. Mark each of these points with an arrow:
    a 10:30 am   **b** 10:15 am   **c** 10:45 am   **d** 10:10 am
    e 10:20 am   **f** 10:40 am   **g** 10:05 am   **h** 10:25 am
    Measure the distance in millimetres from each of these points to the 10:00 am point.

4   This line represents the times of the clock between 09:00 and 13:30.

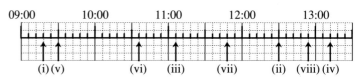

    a Write down the time, in minutes, represented by:
    (i) 1 cm   (ii) 1 mm   (iii) 2 mm
    b Find the times represented by the points (i) to (viii).

5 This line represents the times of the clock between 15:00 and 18:00.

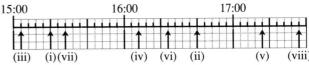

    a Write down the time, in minutes, represented by:

    (i) 1 cm (ii) 1 mm (iii) 2 mm.

    b Find the times represented by the points (i) to (viii).

6 The diagram shows the cost of buying paraffin in litres.

    a Copy and complete:

    (i) 2 mm represents ... pence.

    (ii) 2 mm represents ... litres.

    b Use the diagram to find how many litres you could buy for:

      (i) £1.50   (ii) £3.50

      (iii) £2.20   (iv) £1.40

      (v) £4.80   (vi) £48

      (vii) £25   (viii) £36

    c Use the diagram to find the price of each of the following quantities:

      (i) 21 litres   (ii) 17 litres

      (iii) 3 litres   (iv) 22.5 litres

      (v) 225 litres   (vi) 5.5 litres

      (vii) 16.5 litres   (viii) 24.5 litres

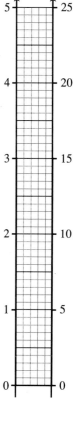

7 The diagram shows exchange values between pounds (£) and Spanish pesetas (Ptas) or vice versa, when the exchange rate is £1 to Ptas 250.

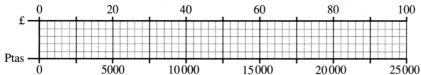

    a Copy and complete:

    (i) 2 mm represents £... .

    (ii) 2 mm represents Ptas ... .

    b Use the diagram to convert these values to pesetas:

    (i) £30   (ii) £90   (iii) £44   (iv) £28   (v) £32   (vi) £56

    c Use the diagram to convert these values to pounds:

    (i) Ptas 17 500   (ii) Ptas 12 500

    (iii) Ptas 2500   (iv) Ptas 16 000

    (v) Ptas 12 000   (vi) Ptas 13 000

8 This scale is marked to show how much money has been raised for a charity fund. (It shows £190.)

Find the amount of money in the fund at each of the points **a** to **h**.

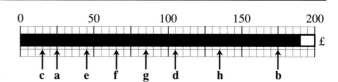

MASTERMINDERS

9 This scale shows how much money has been raised for building a new Sports Hall.

Find the amount of money in the fund at each of the points **a** to **h**.

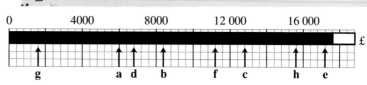

10 The diagram shows a thermometer which can measure temperatures which are well above that of boiling water. What would be the temperature if the mercury level were at each of the points **a** to **h**?

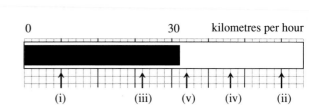

11 This scale shows the speed of a van in km/h.

a Find the speed of the van when the marker is at each of the points (i) to (v).

b How far from the zero point are the points which represent each of the following speeds?

(i) $37\frac{1}{2}$ km/h (ii) $22\frac{1}{2}$ km/h (iii) 36 km/h

(iv) 51 km/h (v) 27 km/h

__ 2.3 Using graphs

The relationship between two quantities can be illustrated on a graph. Look carefully at the following examples.

■ EXAMPLE 1

The graph shows the cost (in pounds) of apples (sold in kilograms).

a Copy and complete:
   (i) 2 mm on the vertical axis represents ...
   (ii) 2 mm on the horizontal axis represents ...
b Use the graph to find:
   (i) The cost of 3 kg, 2.2 kg.
   (ii) The weight which costs £2.50, £2.90.

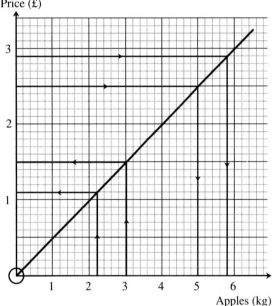

a (i) 2 mm on the vertical axis represents £0.10.
   (ii) 2 mm on the horizontal axis represents 0.2 kg.
b (i) 3 kg cost £1.50, 2.2 kg cost £1.10.
   (ii) £2.50 is the cost of 5 kg, £2.90 is the cost of 5.8 kg.

■ EXAMPLE 2

The graph shows the distance travelled by a model car (in metres) in a certain time (in seconds).

a Copy and complete:
   (i) 2 mm on the vertical axis represents ...
   (ii) 2 mm on the horizontal axis represents ...
b Use the graph to find:
   (i) The distance travelled in 3 seconds, 0.5 seconds.
   (ii) The time taken to travel 10 m, 21 m.

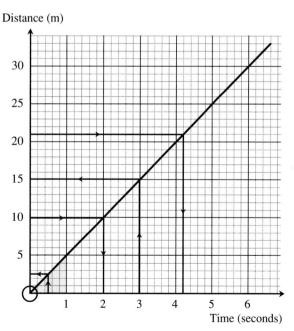

a (i) 2 mm on the vertical axis represents 1.0 m.
   (ii) 2 mm on the horizontal axis represents 0.2 seconds.
b (i) Distance travelled in 3 seconds is 15 m, distance travelled in 0.5 seconds is 2.5 m.
   (ii) Time for 10 m is 2 seconds, time for 21 m is 4.2 seconds.

Exercise 19

1 The graph shows an exchange rate between the French franc and the UK pound.
   a Copy and complete:
   (i) 2 mm on the vertical axis represents . . .
   (ii) 2 mm on the horizontal axis represents . . .
   b Use the graph to find:
   (i) The number of pounds which could be exchanged for Fr 15, Fr 11, Fr 17.
   (ii) The number of francs which could be exchanged for £2, £2.60, £0.90.

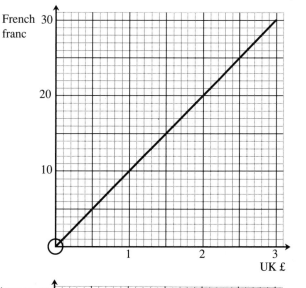

2 The graph shows the distance travelled by a sailing dinghy in a certain time, in metres per second.
   a Copy and complete:
   (i) 2 mm on the vertical axis represents . . .
   (ii) 2 mm on the horizontal axis represents . . .
   b Use the graph to find:
   (i) The distance travelled in the 5 s, 11 s, 26 s.
   (ii) The time taken to travel 32 m, 45 m, 51 m.
   c Write down the speed of the dinghy in metres per second.

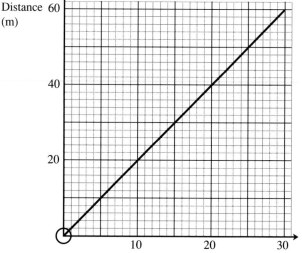

3 The graph illustrates the cost of purified water.
   a Copy and complete:
   (i) On the horizontal axis 2 mm represents . . .
   (ii) On the vertical axis 2 mm represents . . .
   b Read off from the graph:
   (i) The cost of 5 gallons, 3 gallons, 8 gallons.
   (ii) The number of gallons which cost £3, £4.40, £2.60.
   c Write the cost of water in pounds per gallon.

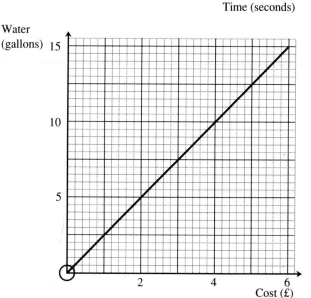

4 The graph shows the fuel consumption of a car in miles per gallon.

   a Copy and complete:

     (i) On the horizontal axis 2 mm represents ....

     (ii) On the vertical axis 2 mm represents ....

   b Use the graph to find:

     (i) The distance travelled using 5 gallons, 4.4 gallons, 5.2 gallons.

     (ii) The number of gallons used in travelling 30 miles, 55 miles, 127.5 miles.

   c Write the fuel consumption in miles per gallon.

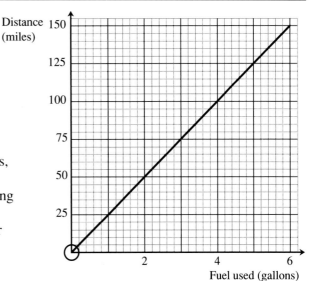

5 A teacher has marked an examination out of 80 and wishes to express each mark as being out of 100. She makes this graph: Use the graph to change the following marks, which are out of 80, to marks out of 100. Give each answer to the nearest whole number.

   a 24 **b** 32 **c** 76 **d** 13 **e** 29

   f 61 **g** 43 **h** 7

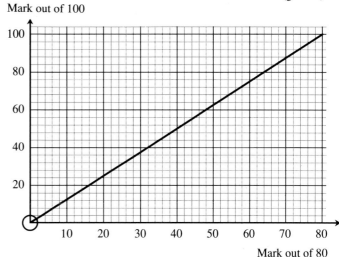

6 Mr Burgess goes on holiday to the USA. He makes a pocket conversion graph, as shown, to help him relate pounds and dollars. Read off the answers from the graph as accurately as you can.

   a Use the graph to change the following amounts to pounds: $3, $13, $12, $8.40, $4.80, $13.20, $15.50

   b Use the graph to change the following amounts to dollars: £4, £6, £9, £2.40, £6.80, £3.20, £7.85

   c Write down the exchange rate in the form '£1 is equivalent to ...'.

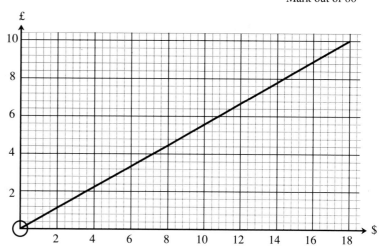

MASTERMINDERS

7   ▦ The graph shows two different exchange rates, A and B, between the German mark (DM) and the UK pound (£).

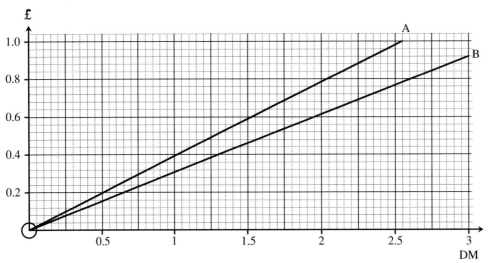

a Write down each exchange rate in the form '£1 is equivalent to DM ...'.
b **Investigate** the effect of each exchange rate on:
(i) A German taking a holiday in the UK.
(ii) A British citizen taking a holiday in Germany.

8   ▦ The graph shows the relationship between yards and metres. (There are 1760 yards in a mile.)

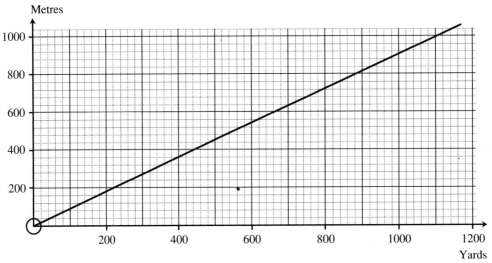

a Mary's grandfather, when he was at school, ran the 220 yards in 23.8 seconds. In what time (to the nearest tenth of a second) do you think he would have run 200 m?
b Show that 80 km/h is very nearly equal to 50 mile/h.

— Revision Exercise 2A

1 The diagram represents the times of the clock between 08:00 and 12:00.

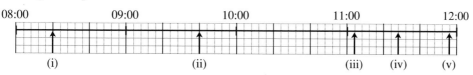

     08:00   09:00   10:00   11:00   12:00

       (i)   (ii)   (iii) (iv) (v)

a Copy and complete:
  (i) 1 cm represents ... minutes.
  (ii) 2 mm represents ... minutes.

b Find the time represented by each of the points (i) to (v) on the diagram.

2 The diagram shows exchange values between pounds (£) and French francs (Fr).

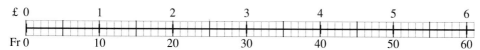

  £ 0   1   2   3   4   5   6

  Fr 0   10   20   30   40   50   60

a Copy and complete:
  (i) 2 cm represents £. ...
  (ii) 2 cm represents Fr ....
  (iii) 2 mm represents ...p.
  (iv) 2 mm represents Fr ....

b Use the diagram to convert these amounts to pounds:
  (i) Fr 25 (ii) Fr 51 (iii) Fr 3

c Use the diagram to convert these amounts to French francs:
  (i) £1.50 (ii) £4.20 (iii) £5.25

3 The graph shows the fuel consumption of a car in miles per gallon.

a Copy and complete:
  (i) On the horizontal axis, 2 mm represents ... gallons.
  (ii) On the vertical axis, 2 mm represents ... miles.

b Use the graph to find the distance travelled using:
  (i) 1.5 gallons (ii) 3.2 gallons

c Use the graph to find the number of gallons used in travelling:
  (i) 60 miles (ii) 90 miles

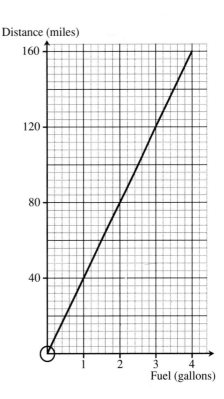

▃ Revision Exercise 2B

1 The diagram represents the times of the clock between 10:00 am and 1:00 pm.

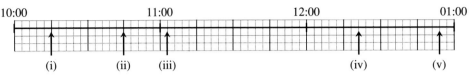

a Copy and complete:
(i) 1 cm represents ... minutes.
(ii) 2 mm represents ... minutes.
b Find the time represented by each of the points (i) to (v) on the diagram.

2 The diagram shows exchange values between pounds (£) and Spanish pesetas (Ptas).

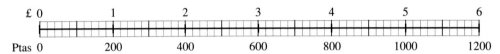

a Copy and complete:
(i) 2 mm represents ...p.
(ii) 2 mm represents Ptas ...
b Use the diagram to convert each of the following amounts to pounds:
(i) Ptas 300 (ii) Ptas 450 (iii) Ptas 1020
c Use the diagram to convert each of the following amounts to Spanish pesetas:
(i) £3.50 (ii) £4.20 (iii) 75p

3 The graph shows the cost of making an overseas telephone call to a certain country.
a Copy and complete:
(i) On the horizontal axis, 2 mm represents ... seconds.
(ii) On the vertical axis, 2 mm represents ... pence.
b Use the graph to find the cost of a call which lasts
(i) 3 minutes (ii) 1 hour (iii) 4 minutes and 48 seconds.
c Use the graph to find the length of a call which costs
(i) £17.50 (ii) £11 (iii) £80.

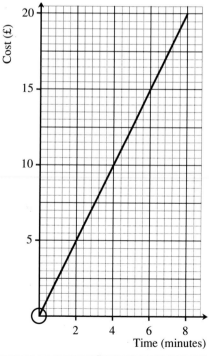

▬ Basics Test 2

A Calculator

  1 $92.16 + 13.24$
  2 $10.526 + 30.45 + 4.824$
  3 $13.6 - 9.08$
  4 $5.036 + 0.087 - 0.003$
  5 1.25×3.6
  6 $\frac{10.08}{2.8}$

B Paper and pencil

  7 105×16
  8 $1080 \div 24$
  9 $253 + 148 + 349$
  10 $905 - 433$
  11 $\frac{3}{10} + \frac{8}{15}$
  12 $\frac{5}{6} - \frac{1}{4}$
  13 $\frac{5}{6} \times \frac{9}{25}$
  14 $\frac{9}{20} \div \frac{15}{16}$

  15 What is four ninths of 55.8 m?

C Mental

  Ten questions will be read out to you.

▬ Puzzlers

1 A girl has as many brothers as sisters, but each of her brothers has only half as many brothers as sisters. How many sisters and brothers are there? Write a similar question yourself and ask another person to work out the answer.

2 Copy and complete the crossnumber (like a crossword!), in which each of the numbers 1 to 19 is used once and the sum of each of the 15 rows is equal to 38.

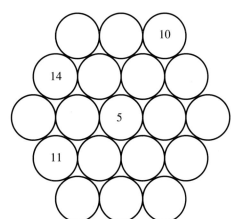

3 Here is an addition sum. If each letter stands for a different digit, find the value of H.

    BARE
    CARE
    DARE
    ‾‾‾‾
    HERE

4 Here is another addition sum. If each letter again stands for a different digit, find the value of each of the letters.

    ABC
     BC
    CBC
    ‾‾‾
    BCC

Coursework: Submarines

Each player needs a sheet of graph paper with x and y axes labelled from 5 to -5 (see Figure 1).

Guy and Jill play a game called 'Submarines'. Guy puts a small cross on his paper to mark the position of the submarine. Jill has to find the position of the submarine by guesswork. To each guess, Guy replies by giving the '**distance**' her guess is from the submarine.

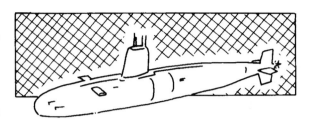

1   **Finding the 'distance'.** The '**distance**' used in this game has a special meaning. It is the shortest route between the guess and the submarine along paths parallel to the axes. For example, in Figure 1 the **distance** between A and S (the submarine) is 7 units.

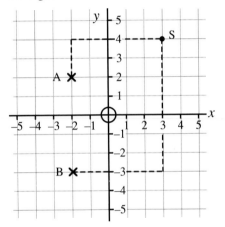

		From			
		L	M	N	O
To	L	0			
	M				
	N				
	O				

Figure 1   **Table 1**

On your x and y axes mark in the following points:
L(4, -2), M(1, -1), N(-4, -4), O(-2, 4)
Work out the **distance** between each pair of points. Copy Table 1 and enter your results.

2   **Example of a game.** (Refer to Figure 1.)
  a On his paper Guy puts a cross at (3, 4) to represent the submarine.
  b Jill guesses that the submarine is at (-2, 2) and says, 'Minus two, two'.
  c Guy replies with the **distance** between (-2, 2) and (3, 4) and says, 'Seven'.
  d Jill then makes a second guess and says, 'Minus two, minus three'.
  e Write down the reply from Guy.

3   Now play a game with a partner.

EXTENSION

4   **a Investigate** the tactics of the game. (It is possible always to locate the submarine after just two guesses.)
  b Devise ways in which the game can be made more challenging.

3 PROPORTION

3.1 Change of units

The diagram shows the distance between the Earth and the planet Pluto in millimetres.

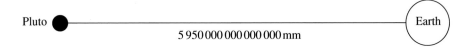

Pluto ●————————————————————— Earth
5 950 000 000 000 000 mm

It is clear that a much larger unit than the millimetre is required for measuring a very large distance of this kind.

The metric units for length, mass and capacity are given below.

Length	Mass	Capacity
10 mm = 1 cm 100 cm = 1 m 1000 m = 1 km	1000 g = 1 kg 1000 kg = 1 tonne	1000 millilitres (written ml) = 1000 cubic centimetres (written cm³) = 1 litre (written l)

To change from one set of units to another you must either multiply or divide by a certain number. This flow chart will help you decide what to do.

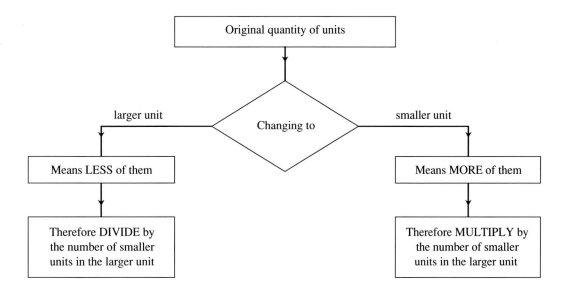

■ EXAMPLE 1

Change 133 minutes to **a** seconds   **b** hours and minutes.

a   133 minutes is **more** than 133 seconds.
Therefore 133 minutes   = 133 × 60 seconds
= 7980 seconds

b   133 minutes is **less** than 133 hours.
Therefore 133 minutes   = 133 ÷ 60 = 2 remainder 13
= 2 hours 13 minutes

■ EXAMPLE 2

Change 406 cm to **a** mm   **b** m.

a   406 cm is **more** than 406 mm.
Therefore 406 cm   = 406 × 10 mm
= 4060 mm

b   406 cm is **less** than 406 m.
Therefore 406 cm   = 406 ÷ 100 m
= 4.06 m

■ EXAMPLE 3

Change the distance from the Earth to Pluto into kilometres. (See page 43.)

[W]   Distance from Earth to Pluto

[W]   = 5 950 000 000 000 000 mm

$$= \frac{5\,950\,000\,000\,000\,000}{1000} \text{ m}$$

$$= \frac{5\,950\,000\,000\,000\,000}{1000 \times 1000} \text{ km}$$

[A]   = 5 950 000 000 km (5950 million km)

___ Exercise 20

1   Copy and complete this table:

	km	m	cm	mm
a	5			
b	8.625			
c		3000		
d		3245		
e		987		
f		56		

	km	m	cm	mm
g		2.6		
h			300	
i			520	
j			60	
k				240
l				87

2 Copy and complete this table:

	Tonnes	Kilograms	Grams
a	8		
b	6.3		
c	0.27		
d		4700	
e		620	

	Tonnes	Kilograms	Grams
f		98	
g		15.6	
h		2.9	
i			600
j			50

3 Copy and complete this table:

	Litres	Millilitres (cm³)
a	4	
b	3.25	
c	0.849	
d	0.18	
e		4176
f		5930

	Litres	Millilitres (cm³)
g	7.025	
h		684
i	0.057	
j		15.4
k	0.0092	
l		5

4 Change to hours and minutes:
   a 420 minutes   **b** 330 minutes   **c** 195 minutes   **d** 225 minutes   **e** 252 minutes

5 Change to minutes and seconds:
   a 960 seconds   **b** 1110 seconds   **c** 195 seconds   **d** 516 seconds   **e** 198 seconds

6 Change to minutes:
   a 0.25 hour   **b** 0.6 hour   **c** 0.55 hour   **d** 0.82 hour   **e** 0.01 hour

7 Change to seconds:
   a $\frac{5}{6}$ of a minute   **b** $\frac{1}{12}$ of a minute   **c** $\frac{3}{5}$ of a minute   **d** $\frac{3}{8}$ of a minute   **e** $\frac{1}{100}$ of an hour

8 Which of the following is the odd one out?
   a 7 cm, 0.07 m, $\frac{7}{100}$ of a metre, 7.0 cm, 7 m
   b 12 minutes, a sixth of an hour, 0.2 hour, a fifth of an hour, 720 seconds
   c 600 g, 0.06 kg, 0.0006 tonne, six tenths of a tonne

9 How many minutes are there in:
   a 3.9 hours   **b** $6\frac{3}{5}$ hours   **c** 2.85 days?

MASTERMINDERS

10 Express:
   a 1 000 000 000 grams in tonnes
   b 3 000 000 000 mm in km
   c 500 000 000 cm in km

11 Express:
   a 0.000 004 tonne in grams
   b 0.000 002 5 km in mm
   c 0.000 015 km in cm

— *Activity 4*

Draw 100 small squares in the shape of one large square to represent a square centimetre, as shown here.

This diagram will help you to remember that there are 100 square millimetres (written $100 \, mm^2$) in one square centimetre (written $1 \, cm^2$).

Imagine you have drawn a diagram of a square metre which is divided into square centimetres. How many square centimetres would there be?

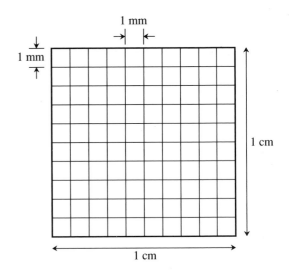

■ *EXAMPLE 4*

Change $52.9 \, mm^2$ to cm^2.

(There are $100 \, mm^2$ in $1 \, cm^2$.)

$52.9 \, mm^2$ is **less** than $52.9 \, cm^2$.

Therefore $52.9 \, mm^2 \quad = 52.9 \div 100 \, cm^2$

$= 0.529 \, cm^2$

■ *EXAMPLE 5*

Change $0.0082 \, m^2$ to cm^2.

(There are $10\,000 \, cm^2$ in $1 \, m^2$.)

$0.0082 \, m^2$ is **more** than $0.0082 \, cm^2$.

Therefore $0.0082 \, m^2 \quad = 0.0082 \times 10\,000 \, cm^2$

$= 82 \, cm^2$

■ *EXAMPLE 6*

Copy and complete the table below.

	Unit change		Operation
	From	*To*	
a	kg	g	
b	m	km	
c	cm^2		× 100
d		kg	÷ 1000

The completed table is as follows:

	Unit change		Operation
	From	*To*	
a	kg	g	**× 1000**
b	m	km	**÷ 1000**
c	cm^2	**mm^2**	× 100
d	**g**	kg	÷ 1000

▬ Exercise 21

Copy and complete this table. (Note that it is in two columns.) Keep your table for future use.

	Unit change From	Unit change To	Operation		Unit change From	Unit change To	Operation
1	km	m		**11**	ml		÷ 1000
2	m	mm		**12**	kg		÷ 1000
3	m	cm		**13**		cm	÷ 10
4	cm	mm		**14**		cm²	÷ 100
5	km²	m²		**15**	mm		÷ 1 000 000
6	m²	cm²		**16**	min		× 60
7	s	min		**17**	min		÷ 60
8	g	kg		**18**		min	÷ 60
9	g	tonnes		**19**		cm	× 100 000
10	cm²	m²		**20**		cm³	× 1

21 Change to cm²: **a** 4.5 m² **b** 1.09 m² **c** 195 mm² **d** 789.4 mm²

22 Which is the odd one out?
400 cm², 40 000 mm², four hundredths of a m², 0.004 m²

23 A sheet of paper measures 95 cm by 84 cm. What is its area in m²?

24 Which is heavier and by how much – a shoe weighing 345.9 g or a book weighing 0.49 kg?

Work out **mentally** the **approximate** answers to questions 25 to 27.

25 Change:
  a 3843 m to km **b** 475 cm to m   **c** 306 m to cm   **d** 7397 g to kg   **e** 648 seconds to minutes

26 Change:
  a 0.948 m to cm   **b** 0.883 cm² to mm²   **c** 0.018 km to m
  d 0.049 kg to g   **e** 0.73 hours to minutes

27 Find:
  a $\frac{2}{3}$ cm in mm   **b** $\frac{5}{8}$ km in m   **c** $\frac{4}{9}$ of an hour in minutes
  d $\frac{4}{7}$ m² in cm²   **e** $\frac{23}{49}$ of a tonne in kg

MASTERMINDERS

28 Change to mm²: **a** $\frac{1}{2000}$ m² **b** $\frac{1}{125\,000}$ m² **c** $\frac{1}{400\,000}$ m²

29 Change to m²: **a** 6 000 000 mm² **b** 2 500 000 mm²   **c** 750 000 mm²

30 On a map, a wood is shown as a square of side 2 cm. If the scale of the map is such that 1 cm on the map represents 500 m on the land, find the area of the wood in km².

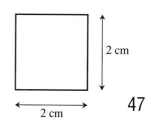
2 cm

2 cm

47

— 3.2 Problem solving

The 'Unitary Method' can be used to solve a variety of problems involving two different quantities. Its rules are given in the Note below, and used in the Examples.

> ### NOTE
>
> 1 The Question quantity is always put on the lefthand side (LHS).
> 2 The Answer quantity is always put on the righthand side (RHS).
> 3 If necessary, the Question quantity is changed to unity (one).
> 4 All quantities are clearly labelled with their units.
> 5 The two quantities are linked using words.

■ *EXAMPLE 1*

A holiday for six people costs £1470. Find the cost of a similar holiday for

a one person
b seven people.

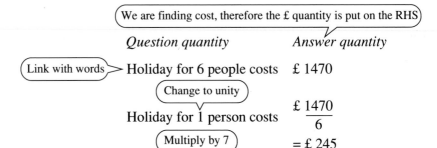

We are finding cost, therefore the £ quantity is put on the RHS

Question quantity	*Answer quantity*
Link with words → Holiday for 6 people costs	£ 1470

Change to unity

Holiday for 1 person costs $\dfrac{£\,1470}{6}$

Multiply by 7   = £ 245

Holiday for 7 people costs £ 245 × 7 = £ 1715

■ *EXAMPLE 2*

A car uses 45 litres of petrol to travel 540 km.
a How far should it travel using 1 litre?
b How many litres, to the nearest litre, would the car need to travel 175 km?

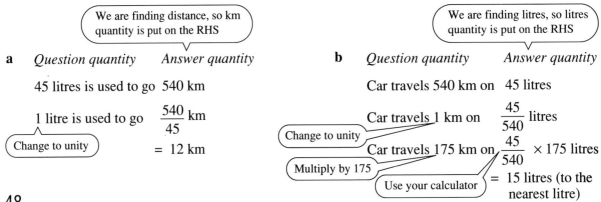

a

We are finding distance, so km quantity is put on the RHS

Question quantity   Answer quantity

45 litres is used to go 540 km

1 litre is used to go $\dfrac{540}{45}$ km

Change to unity   = 12 km

b

We are finding litres, so litres quantity is put on the RHS

Question quantity   Answer quantity

Car travels 540 km on 45 litres

Car travels 1 km on $\dfrac{45}{540}$ litres

Change to unity

Car travels 175 km on $\dfrac{45}{540}$ × 175 litres

Multiply by 175

Use your calculator   = 15 litres (to the nearest litre)

> **REMEMBER**
>
> - Put the Answer quantity on the righthand side.
> - Change the Question quantity to unity (one).

___ Exercise 22

1 A Volkswagen factory produces 240 cars every 60 minutes. How many are produced
a in 1 minute **b** in 15 minutes?

2 A 5-metre length of wood costs £1.40. What is the cost of **a** 1 metre **b** 6 metres?

3 Seven identical books cost £26.95. How much **a** does one cost **b** do five cost?

4 The late BBC commentator Raymond Glendenning once spoke 177 words in 30 seconds.
How many words did he speak **a** in 1 second **b** in 20 seconds?
(Find out how long it takes you to read a passage containing 177 words from a book.)

5 The bill for 5 identical meals came to £92.50. What was the cost of **a** 1 meal **b** 6 meals?

6 In a certain recipe, 46 oranges are used to make 115 pounds of marmalade.
How many pounds of marmalade can be made with **a** one orange **b** 13 oranges?

7 A factory produces 350 television sets in 14 hours. How many are produced in
a one hour **b** four hours?

8 In its first $2\frac{1}{2}$ months the film *Jaws* made £5 040 000 per week.
How much did the film make **a** in one day
b in 70 days ($2\frac{1}{2}$ months)?

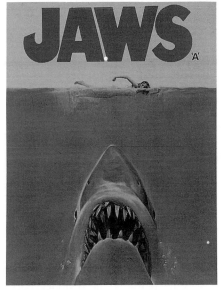

9 ▦ A Harrier fighter plane uses 675 gallons of fuel on a 45-minute flight.
a For how long would it travel using one gallon?
b How many gallons would it use in one minute?

10 ▦ A model car travels 1.2 km in 30 minutes.
a How long would it take to travel one km?
b How far would it travel in one minute?

For Questions 11 to 14, give your answer to a sensible degree of accuracy, say 2 or 3 digits.

11 ▦ £9 is exchanged for $15.85. How many **a** dollars would you expect to get for £1
b pounds would you expect to get for $1?

12 ▦ Fr 77 are exchanged for DM 29.4. How many **a** francs would you expect to get for DM 1
b marks would you expect to get for Fr 1?

13 ▦ Look at this carton of tomato juice.

   a How many cubic centimetres are there in 1 fluid ounce?
   b How many fluid ounces are there in 1 cubic centimetre?

14 ▦ There are more motor vehicles in Los Angeles than in any other city in the world. At one interchange almost half a million vehicles were counted in a 24-hour period. How many vehicles were counted per hour?

15 ▦ A telephone call to New Zealand costs £2.25 per minute. How long, to the nearest second, would you get for £1?

16 ▦ The fastest growing tree is the Albizzia. It can grow 35 feet in 52 weeks. How high, to the nearest foot, would you expect it to grow in three weeks?

17 ▦ Fred's hair grows about 1 inch every 7 weeks. How many inches would you expect it to grow in a year? (Give your answer to the nearest inch.)

18 ▦ Human finger nails grow about 1.96 mm every four weeks. Paul hits his thumb nail with a hammer. A full-size drawing of his bruised thumb is shown here.
Estimate in how many weeks you would expect the bruising to grow out.
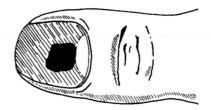

19 ▦ The Concise Oxford Dictionary has pages numbered from 1 to 1260 and, without the cover, is 44.1 mm thick.
   a How thick is a similar dictionary, without the cover, which has 900 pages?
   b How many pages does a similar dictionary have if it is 56 mm thick without the cover?

MASTERMINDERS

20 ▦ **Investigate** the following facts:

	Population (millions)	Population increase per day
China	1000	50 000
World	5000	216 000

21 ▦ Two villages, which are 6 km apart, are shown as 12 cm apart on a map.
   a What is the actual distance between two places which are 12.5 cm apart on the map?
   b What is the distance, on the map, between two places which are actually 2.25 km apart?

22 ▦ **Investigate** these facts. An A10 fighter aircraft can fire 100 bullets per second. Each one weighs about 300 g and is 14 cm long.
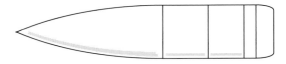

— 3.3 Scale

A scale of 1 : 50 means that 1 cm represents an actual length of 50 cm, 1 m represents an actual length of 50 m, and so on.

— *Activity 5*

1   Collect different examples of things which have been drawn to scale. Explain why it is often necessary to draw things to scale and why the scale used is not always the same. Can you find something which is to scale but not necessarily drawn? Keep all your examples for part 3 of this Activity.

2   When drawing the plans of a house, a certain architect uses a scale of 1 in 50, written 1 : 50. Copy and complete the working for each of parts **a**, **b** and **c**.

a Find the actual length of a line which is 4 cm long on these plans.

b If a room is 7.5 m long, find the length of the room on the plans.

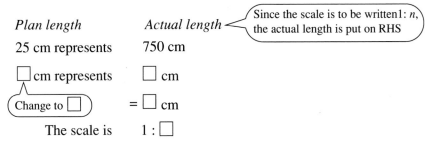

a

We are finding the actual length, so this is put on RHS

Plan length	Actual length
1 cm represents	50 cm
☐ cm represents	☐ cm

Multiply by ☐   = ☐

b

We are finding the plan length, so this is put on RHS

Actual length	Plan length

☐ cm is represented by   1 cm

Change to unity ➔ 1 cm is represented by   ☐ cm

750 cm is represented by   ☐ × 750 cm

Multiply by 750   = ☐ cm

c If the same room is 25 cm long on the plans drawn by another architect, find the scale used by this architect.

Plan length	Actual length
25 cm represents	750 cm
☐ cm represents	☐ cm

Since the scale is to be written 1 : n, the actual length is put on RHS

Change to ☐   = ☐ cm

The scale is   1 : ☐

3   **Investigate** the plans, scale drawings and illustrations which you collected in part 1.

___ Exercise 23

1 A model of an aeroplane has a length of 45 cm and is built to a scale of 1 : 40. Find the length of the real aeroplane.

2 A doll's house is constructed as a 1 : 15 scale model of a real house. If the doll's house is 90 cm long, find the length of the real house.

3 The diagram shows a rough sketch of the end of a house. Using the information shown, make a scale drawing at 1 : 100. (Remember to show all your working.)

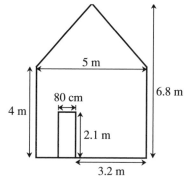

4 This small animal is drawn to a scale of 15 : 1. Estimate its true length.

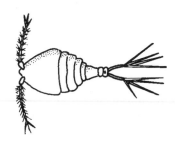

5 An architect takes several measurements in a house and draws a plan to a scale of 1 : 50. Copy and complete the table below. (Remember to show all your working.)

		Actual dimension	Length on plans
a	Door width	80 cm	
b	Door height	220 cm	
c	Window width	125 cm	
d	Window height	90 cm	
e	Room length	3.75 m	
f	Room width	2.55 m	
g	Wall thickness	35 cm	

6 Howard has a toy car of length 7.5 cm. It is a scale model of a real car of length 3.6 m. To what scale has the model been built?

7 Write each of the following scales in the form 1 : n, where n is a whole number.
  a 1 cm represents 1 m
  b 1 cm represents 5 m
  c 1 cm represents 10 m
  d 1 cm represents 0.5 m
  e 1 cm represents 1 km
  f 1 cm represents 0.5 km

8 The garden of a house is 25 m long and 20 m wide. Find the dimensions, in centimetres, of the garden on a plan drawn to each of the following scales:
a 1 : 25 **b** 1 : 50 **c** 1 : 100 **d** 1 : 200 **e** 1 : 250 **f** 1 : 500
Which scale would be the best for drawing a plan of the garden on (i) a piece of exercise-book paper (ii) the back of an envelope?

9 Measure each of the marked dimensions on this plan. Find each of the actual dimensions if the scale of the plan is 1 : 100.

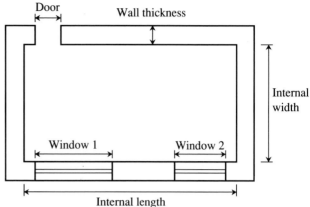

10 a Find the scale of this map if it is 2 km from the road junction to the level crossing.
b One day there is a hold-up at the level crossing and the queue of traffic on the western side extends to the church, while that on the eastern side extends to where the power-line crosses the road. Find the length of both traffic queues.

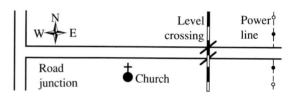

11 Here is another Stegosaurus (see page 4). If this diagram is drawn to a scale of 1 : 120, what is the approximate length of this dinosaur?

MASTERMINDERS

12 Measure the length of Rosehill Avenue on the street plan.
a If the actual length of the avenue is 195 m, to what scale has the plan been drawn?
b A telephone engineer says that the telephone kiosk is 135 m from the western end of the avenue. Is she correct?
c A postman at the eastern end of the avenue tells someone that the post box is 75 m along the avenue. Is he correct?

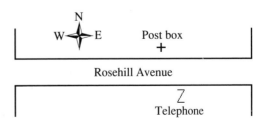

13 The standard gauge of British Rail tracks is 144 cm. The gauge of a certain miniature railway is 48 cm. Find the scale to which the miniature railway is built.

The miniature railway has some passenger coaches and goods trucks which are scale models of the ones used by British Rail. A rectangular window on a British Rail coach measures 135 cm by 90 cm.

a Find the area of the window. (Area = Length × Width)

b Find the dimensions of the window on a miniature railway coach.

c Find the area of the window on a miniature railway coach.

d Find the ratio of the area of the window of a British Rail coach to the area of the window of a miniature railway coach.

This is a diagram of a British Rail goods truck.

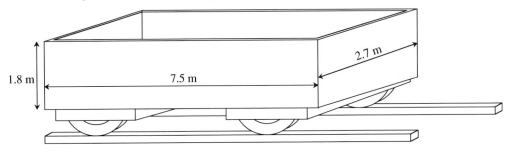

Find the ratio of the volume of a British Rail truck to the volume of a miniature railway truck. (Volume = Length × Width × Height)

___ *Activity 6*

1 Look carefully at the picture of St James's Palace and try to work out its scale. Use your answer to estimate the width and height of the tower.

2 Collect photographs of other wellknown buildings or objects and try to work out their scales.

— 3.4 Scale drawing

From the previous section you should have noticed that scale drawings are useful when it is not practical to make a full-size drawing.

— *Activity 7*

This scale drawing shows the size of the proposed 'Millennium 800' to be built in Japan, and also the Eiffel Tower drawn to the same scale.

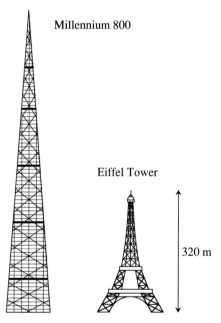

Millennium 800

Eiffel Tower

320 m

1   Work out the scale of this drawing.

2   Why do you think the tower is called the 'Millennium 800'?

3   The table shows the height, to the nearest 10 m, of five other very tall structures.

Structure	Height (m)
Sears Tower, Chicago	440
Empire State Building	410
Telecom Tower, London	190
St Paul's Cathedral	110
Nelson's Column	60

Using a scale of 1 : 5000, make a scale drawing of each of the above seven structures.

___ Exercise 24

Each pupil should do one question from questions 1 to 5, and either question 6 or 7. Pupils who are good at drawing should do either question 3 or 5.

1 This table gives the heights of six mountains. Using a scale of 1 : 100 000, illustrate these heights on a scale drawing.

Mountain	Height (to 100 m)
Mount Everest (Nepal)	8800 m
Aconcagua (Argentina)	7000 m
Mount McKinley (Alaska)	6200 m
Mont Blanc (France)	4800 m
Ben Nevis (Scotland)	1300 m
Scafell Pike (England)	1000 m

2 This table gives the depths of six land depressions. Using a scale of 1 : 5000, illustrate these depths on a scale drawing.

Depression	Depth below sea level (to 10 m)
Dead Sea (Israel, Jordan)	400 m
Turfan Depression (China)	150 m
Death Valley (USA)	90 m
Caspian Sea (former USSR)	30 m
Lake Eyre (Australia)	10 m
Zuiderzee (Netherlands)	5 m

3 This diagram shows the Earth's largest creature, the blue whale.

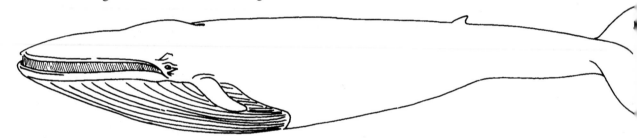

If the length of the creature is 34 m, find the scale of the drawing.
Using the same scale, illustrate the lengths of these creatures on a scale drawing.

Creature	Length (to nearest metre)
Blue whale (largest animal on Earth)	34 m
Whale shark (largest fish)	18 m
Crocodile (largest reptile)	7 m
African elephant (largest land animal)	6 m
Man	2 m

4 The approximate dimensions of three very large buildings are given below. Measure the dimensions of your school hall and then copy and complete the table.

Building	Length	Width
Largest industrial building on Earth (Soviet tank and railway factory)	900 m	900 m
Largest commercial building on Earth (Dutch flower auction building)	700 m	500 m
Largest commercial building in UK (Ford Parts Centre, Daventry)	600 m	200 m
Our school hall		

Using any suitable scale, illustrate the four buildings on a scale drawing which shows all of them on the same sheet of paper.

5 This table gives various heights (to the nearest 10 cm).

Animal or person	Height
Giraffe	5.6 m
African elephant	3.2 m
Tallest man ever (Mr Wadlow, USA)	2.7 m
Irish Wolfhound (tallest dog)	0.9 m
Shortest woman ever (Miss Musters, Holland)	0.6 m

a Using a scale of 1 : 50, show these heights on a scale diagram.

b Measure your own height and that of another person. Using a scale of 1 : 20, show on a scale diagram the height of yourself, the other person you have measured, Mr Wadlow and Miss Musters.

c From the photograph, estimate the heights of Mr Wadlow's brothers.

6 This table shows the thicknesses of six everyday objects which are very thin.

Object	Thickness
Protractor	0.75 mm
Cover of this book	0.36 mm
School shirt	0.18 mm
Page from this book	0.10 mm
Sheet of thin paper	0.05 mm
Clingfilm	0.01 mm

Using a scale of 100 : 1, draw a scale diagram to illustrate these thicknesses.

7 This table shows the thicknesses (or diameters) of five everyday objects which have a circular cross-section. Copy and complete the table.

Object	Diameter	Radius	Scaled radius
Pin or needle	0.6 mm	0.3 mm	6 cm
5-amp fuse wire	0.2 mm	0.1 mm	
Sewing cotton	0.12 mm		
Human hair	0.06 mm		
Spider's web	0.006 mm		

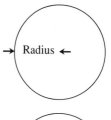

Use a pair of compasses to draw five circles to represent these cross-sections, on a scale of 200 : 1.

3 PROPORTION

▬ Revision Exercise 3A

Calculators are **not allowed**.

1 Change: **a** 145 cm to m   **b** 1900 m to km   **c** 1760 kg to tonnes
2 How many: **a** mm in 14 cm   **b** g in 46 kg   **c** cubic centimetres in a litre?
3 Change: **a** 2.5 km to m   **b** 0.3 cm to mm   **c** 135 seconds to minutes and seconds
4 A piece of paper measures 7 cm by 12 cm. What is its area in mm²?
5 A holiday for four people costs £1840. Find the cost of a similar holiday for **a** one person
   b three people.
6 This InterCity train is drawn to a scale of 1 : 1000. What is its length in metres?

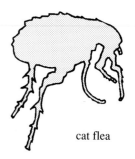

7 On a certain map a distance of 1 cm represents 50 m. Write this scale in the form $1 : n$, where
   n is a whole number.
8 A piece of fuse wire has a diameter (thickness) of 0.1 mm. Use a pair of compasses to draw a
   circle to represent the cross-section using a scale of 500 : 1.
9 It is reported that on average Jeffrey Archer sells 720 of his books throughout the world every
   60 minutes.
   a How long does it take to sell one of his books? **b** How many of his books are sold in a week?

▬ Revision Exercise 3B

Calculators are **not allowed**.

1 Change: **a** 2350 g to kg   **b** 2350 mm to m   **c** 2350 seconds to minutes
2 Which of the following is the odd one out?
   18 minutes, 0.3 hours, $\frac{1}{3}$ of an hour, 1080 seconds, 0.0125 days
3 Change: **a** 450 mm² to cm²   **b** 0.038 m² to cm²   **c** $\frac{3}{5}$ of an hour to minutes
4 A car uses 11 gallons to travel 264 miles. How far would you expect it to travel using
   a 1 gallon   **b** 13 gallons?
5 The plans of a house are drawn to a scale of 1 : 200.
   a Find the actual length of a room which is 2.5 cm long on these plans.
   b If the house is 12 m long, find the length of the house on these plans.
6 The diagram shows a cat flea drawn to a scale of 20 : 1.
   Estimate its true length.

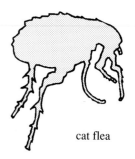
cat flea

7 £24 can be exchanged for 6000 Japanese yen. Copy and complete:
   a £1 can be exchanged for ... yen.
   b 1 yen can be exchanged for ...p.
8 A factory produces 70 cars in 5 hours.
   a How many cars would you expect it to produce in 1.5 hours?
   b How long would you expect it to take to produce 266 cars?

___ Basics Test 3

A Calculator
Write each answer to the nearest 10.
  1 $35.89 + 93.96$ **2** $209 \div 7.4$
  3 297.4×0.65 **4** $\frac{297.4}{0.65}$
  5 $\frac{5}{11} \times 679$ **6** $\frac{146.9 + 649 - 36}{7.93}$

B Paper and pencil
  7 $335 + 97 + 193$ **8** $710 - 557$
  9 $15 \times 12 \times 8$ **10** $918 \div 27$
  11 $\frac{3}{8} + \frac{1}{16}$ **12** $\frac{3}{8} \div \frac{1}{16}$
  13 Change 0.2 hour to minutes.   **14** What is $\frac{3}{8}$ of 104 kg?
  15 What is an approximate answer to 478×0.389?

C Mental
Ten questions will be read out to you.

___ Puzzlers

1 Each letter in the diagram represents a number. The totals of the four rows and of three of the columns are shown. Find the total of the first column.

A	A	A	A	28
A	A	B	B	30
B	C	D	A	20
D	D	C	B	16
19	20	30		

2 In the addition sum each letter represents a different digit. Find the value of each of the letters.

```
    F I V E
    T W O
+     O N E
  ─────────
  E I G H T
```

3 Old MacDonald has a farm on which there are a number of heads, legs and wings.

a If there are 3 heads on the farm, there are 4 possibilities for the numbers of wings and legs. Copy and complete the table.

No. of heads	No. of legs	No. of wings
3	12	
3	10	
3		4
3		6

b Make and complete a similar table for (i) 4 heads on the farm (ii) 5 heads on the farm.
c If Old MacDonald had 9 heads and 28 legs on his farm, how many wings would he have?
d Copy and complete the following statement:

☐ × number of ☐ = number of ☐ + number of ☐

Coursework: Ancient units

About 500 BC the Egyptians devised the following system to measure lengths:

4 digits = 1 palm

3 palms = 1 hand span

2 hand spans = 1 cubit

4 cubits = 1 stature of a human

= 1 arm span (finger-tips to finger-tips)

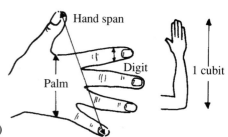

1   Use your own hand and arm to discover which of the four conversions is **a** the most accurate **b** the least accurate.

2   Measure the length of your classroom using **a** your hand spans   **b** your cubits   **c** your arm spans. Comment on your results.

3   Write down any advantages and disadvantages that this Egyptian measuring system has over our current system.

4   Copy and complete this table:

Unit	Number of digits	Fraction of arm span
1 palm		
1 hand span		
1 cubit		
1 arm span		

5   What fraction of an arm span is **a** 2 palms   **b** 5 hand spans   **c** 1 palm and 2 digits **d** 1 cubit, 1 hand span and 3 digits?

6   Copy and complete the table:

Name	Notes	Height	World record	Estimated width, in cm, of Digit	Palm	Hand span
Mr Wadlow	USA 1918	272 cm	Tallest known			
Miss Musters	Holland 1876	60 cm	Shortest known			

Use your answers to make a full-size drawing of each of their hands, together with a full-size drawing of your own.

EXTENSION

7   **a** Two girls measure the width of a book. Jill's measurement is 1 hand span and 3 digits. Indira's measurement is 1 hand span. If Indira's height is 144 cm, work out (i) the width of the book (ii) Jill's height.

   b A Pharaoh went on a training run around the square base of his pyramid. If the side length of the pyramid was $143\frac{3}{4}$ arm spans and the Pharaoh ran at 100 digits per second, find how long it took him to complete one lap.

4 ARITHMETIC II

4.1 Percentages

The term 'per cent' means 'per hundred' or 'out of 100'. A percentage is therefore a fraction with the denominator (number on the bottom) equal to 100.

For example, 45 per cent (written 45%) $= \dfrac{45}{100} = \dfrac{9}{20}$ (as a fraction in its lowest terms).

REMEMBER

Percentage $\longrightarrow$ $\boxed{\div 100}$ $\longrightarrow$ Fraction

To change a fraction to a percentage we multiply by 100. For example, $\dfrac{3}{5} = \dfrac{3}{\underset{1}{\cancel{5}}} \times \overset{20}{\cancel{100}} = 60\%$ (Cancel)

REMEMBER

Fraction $\longrightarrow$ $\boxed{\times 100}$ $\longrightarrow$ Percentage

Exercise 25

1 Change to a percentage:
   a $\frac{1}{4}$ **b** $\frac{1}{5}$ **c** $\frac{1}{8}$ **d** $\frac{3}{5}$
   e $\frac{9}{40}$ **f** $\frac{3}{8}$ **g** $\frac{11}{20}$ **h** $\frac{7}{16}$

2 Change to a fraction in its lowest terms:
   a 37% **b** 58% **c** 28% **d** 98%
   e 84% **f** 12.5% **g** 1.25% **h** 2.8%

3 Which is the larger:
   a $\frac{9}{20}$ or 38%? **b** $\frac{3}{25}$ or 14%? **c** 28% or $\frac{13}{50}$? **d** 33% or $\frac{1}{3}$?

MASTERMINDERS

4 ▦ Change to the nearest whole percentage:
   a $\frac{1}{3}$ **b** $\frac{18}{19}$ **c** 0.0456 **d** 0.456

5 ▦ Which is the larger:
   a $\frac{9}{11}$ or 81% **b** $\frac{12}{19}$ or $\frac{11}{17}$? **c** 0.668 or $\frac{2}{3}$? **d** 37% or $\frac{3}{8}$?

— *Activity 8A*

Investigate whether this was good news or bad news!

1   Explain how this might have been a mark of 100%.

2   Explain how this might have been a mark of 16%.

3   Give examples, as percentages, of other possible marks.

4   Comment on your investigation.

> Dear Mum,
>
> My French teacher told me to tell you I got 16 in a test.
>
> Lot's of love
>
> Alex.Lai
> xxx

— *Activity 8B*

Hannah is on a cycle ride. She says 'I have got 10 kilometres to go'. **Investigate** this statement.

As we do not know how far she has already cycled, we cannot work out the proportion (of the whole journey) the last 10 km represents. Therefore, we must consider different journey distances.

1   She could have already cycled 90 km. In this case, '10 km to go', written as a fraction of the whole journey, is:

$$\frac{10}{100} = \frac{1}{10}$$

As a percentage of the whole journey, it is:

$$\frac{1}{10} \times 100 = 10\%$$

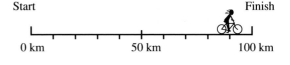

2   This diagram shows a total journey distance of 11 km.

   a In this case work out what fraction of the whole journey '10 km to go' is.

   b Use your calculator to change the fraction to a percentage, to the nearest whole number.

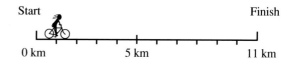

3   Explain, with the help of a diagram, where Hannah would have been if she had
   a 100%   **b** 0% of her journey to complete.

In the same way as we used fractions to describe part of a given quantity, we can also use percentages.

■ *EXAMPLE 1*

One day a shop sells 750 copies of a newspaper. 24% were sold before 9:00 am. How many were sold **a** before 9:00 am   **b** after 9:00 am?

a   [W]   Number of copies sold before 9:00 am

    [W] $= 24\%$ of 750

         $= \dfrac{24}{100} \times 750$

    [A] $= 180$

b   [W]   Number of copies sold after 9:00 am

    [W] $= 750 - 180$

    [A] $= 570$

(Notice that 76% of 750 is also equal to 570.)

■ *EXAMPLE 2*

There were 7400 spectators at a football match. 2590 supported the visitors. Find the percentage **a** who supported the visitors   **b** who did not support the visitors.

a   [W]   Percentage who supported visitors

    [W] $= \dfrac{2590}{7400} \times 100$

    [A] $= 35\%$

b   [W]   Percentage who did not support visitors

    [W] $= 100\% - 35\%$

    [A] $= 65\%$

(Notice that $\frac{7400-2590}{7400} \times 100$ is also equal to 65%.)

▬ Exercise 26

For Questions 1 to 6, find which, of **a**, **b** and **c**, is different from the other two.

1 a 35% of £12   **b** 15% of £32   **c** 20% of £21

2 a 25% of £35   **b** 60% of £14.55   **c** 45% of £19.40

3 a 40% of £112.50   **b** 60% of £67.50   **c** 24% of £187.50

4 a 20% of £140.40   **b** $12\frac{1}{2}$% of £224.80   **c** 26% of £108

5 a 20% of 44 m   **b** 18% of 46.5 m   **c** 9% of 93 m

6 a 5 m 60 cm as a percentage of 16 m
  b 17 m 85 cm as a percentage of 51 m
  c 11 m 25 cm as a percentage of 30 m

For Questions 7 to 13, give the answer to the nearest whole number.

7 What is 17% of 167 kg?

8 Find 89% of 60 miles.

9 Find 9.9% of £566.

10 Write 5.9 cm as a percentage of 11 cm.

11 Write 59 cm as a percentage of 1.3 m.

12 Write 45 g as a percentage of 1.2 kg.

13 Write £6.87 as a percentage of £1.09.

14 An art exhibition was open for six days of a certain week and 1600 people altogether paid a visit. The percentage of the total for each of the days is given here:

Monday	15%	Thursday	12%
Tuesday	10%	Friday	6%
Wednesday	25%	Saturday	32%

Find the number who attended on each of the days.

15 One year at Oakhill School, 280 pupils were entered for external examinations in each of seven subjects. The percentage pass rates are shown below.

Mathematics	75%
English	90%
History	65%
Geography	85%
French	$87\frac{1}{2}$%
Science	$62\frac{1}{2}$%
CDT	$82\frac{1}{2}$%

Find the number of successful pupils for each of the seven subjects.

16 A village has 1200 inhabitants:

      300 are women
      180 are girls
      288 are boys
      432 are men

Convert each of these figures to **a** fraction, and **b** a percentage, of the total.

17 One year Sophie obtained the following examination results:

Mathematics   56 out of 80
English   36 out of 75
History   27 out of 45
Geography   24 out of 60
French   96 out of 120
Science   84 out of 150
CDT   81 out of 180

Convert each of her marks to a percentage. Comment on your answers.

18 a What fraction of the water has been taken up by the plant?
b What is this as a percentage?

80 ml   72 ml

19 a What fraction of the original length is the increase in length?
b What is this as a percentage?

 12 cm

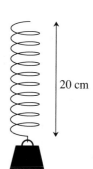 20 cm

20 A crystal weighs 24 g. After heating it weighs 21 g.
a What fraction of the weight is lost?
b What is this as a percentage?

21

Top five paper-producing countries (millions of tonnes per year)	
USA	54
Japan	16
West Germany (former)	8
China	6
France	5

Work out the production of each country as a percentage of the USA's production. Give your answer to the nearest whole number.

22 🖩

Top ten coal-producing countries (millions of tonnes per year)			
China	763	India	136
USA	751	Australia	125
USSR (former)	485	W. Germany (former)	85
Poland	192	Britain	51
S. Africa	140	Czechoslovakia	27

Work out the production of each country as a percentage of China's production. Give your answer to the nearest whole number.

23 🖩

Religions of the World (millions)			
Christianity	995	Confucianism	155
Islam	590	Shintoism	57
Hinduism	480	Taoism	31
Buddhism	255	Judaism	14

Investigate these figures, using percentages.

MASTERMINDERS

24 🖩 **Investigate** these figures for the elderly population of the UK, using percentages.

Year	Population	% over 65	
1981	53 million	15%	
2021	* 58 million	*17%	* Estimates.

25 🖩 There are about 995 000 000 Christians in the world: 58% Catholic, 8% Eastern Orthodox and 34% Protestant. Work out an estimate of the number of each type.

26 🖩

The waters of the Earth	
Sea water	1350 million km³
Pacific Ocean	702 million km³
Atlantic Ocean	324 million km³
Indian Ocean	297 million km³
Fresh water	35 million km³

a What percentage of all the Earth's water is fresh water?
b **Investigate** these figures using percentages.

27 🖩 Lesley's brother bought a motorcycle for £625 in January 1986. By January 1987, its value had fallen to 80% of its purchase price; and by January 1988, its value had fallen to 80% of the January 1987 figure. For every January thereafter the value was only 50% of the figure for the previous January.
By what year was the motorcycle only worth its scrap value of £50?

___ *Activity 9* ▦

The following table shows the results of a survey carried out amongst 11-year-old pupils.

What adult do you get on best with?		For how long did you watch TV or a video after school yesterday?	
Mother	30%	None	6%
Father	11%	Less than 1h	15%
Both parents	42%	1h to 2h	22%
Brother or sister	4%	2h to 3h	19%
None of these	13%	3h to 4h	15%
		More than 4h	23%

Carry out your own survey and compare your results to those shown above.

___ **4.2** Ratio

A ratio is a comparison of two quantities written as, say, 2 : 3. Both quantities **must** be in the same units.

■ *EXAMPLE 1*

A father divides £20 between Peter and James in the ratio 2 : 3. How much does each receive?

The ratio is 2 : 3, so sum = 2 + 3 = 5.

[W]   Amount Peter receives

This becomes the denominator.

[W] $= \dfrac{2}{5}$ of £20

[A] $= £8$

[W]   Amount James receives

[W] $= £20 - £8$

[A] $= £12$

(Notice that $\frac{3}{5}$ of £20 is also equal to £12.)

■ *EXAMPLE 2*

A baker bakes 80 white loaves and 100 brown loaves. Find the ratio of white to brown.

[W]   Ratio of white to brown loaves

[W] $= 80 : 100$

[A] $= 8 : 10 = 4 : 5$

___ **Exercise 27**

1 On a farm one year 132 black lambs and 176 white lambs are born. Find the ratio of black to white lambs. If 140 of the lambs are ewes and 168 are rams, find the ratio of ewes to rams.

2 Lisa is 100 cm tall and her older sister Nina is 175 cm tall. Find the ratio of Lisa's height to Nina's. If they weigh 35 kg and 77 kg, respectively, find the ratio of their weights.

3 From where I live to London, the journey takes 45 minutes by train but two hours by bus. Find the ratio of the two times.
The fare by train, however, is £4.50, but the bus fare is only £2.50. Find the ratio of the two fares.

4 On a bus there are 35 passengers downstairs and 28 passengers upstairs. Find the ratio of passengers sitting upstairs to passengers sitting downstairs.
If the bus has 81 seats altogether, find the ratio of occupied seats to empty seats.

5 This map shows two railway routes from London to Exeter.
Find the ratio of the longer distance to the shorter one. Find the same ratio for the two London to Taunton routes.

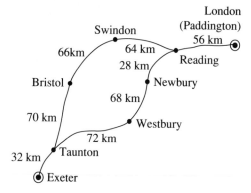

6 There are 350 boys at Southmead School. For their sports option in the winter 175 choose football, 105 choose rugby and 70 choose cross-country. Find the ratio of boys choosing football to rugby to cross-country.

7 A man is mixing concrete, using 90 kg of shingle, 75 kg of sand and 45 kg of cement. Find the ratio of shingle to sand to cement.

8 ▦ A builders' merchant has only 4500 kg of concrete mix in stock. It is sold to two builders in the ratio 11 : 4. Find how much each builder buys.

9 ▦ Mr Bates shares £58.50 between his two children in the same ratio as that of their ages. If William is 14 and Charlotte is 12, how much does each receive?

10 ▦ A piece of wood is 3 m long. It is cut into three parts in the ratio 11 : 8 : 5. Find the length of each part.

MASTERMINDERS

11 🖩 Two excursion trains carry 1200 supporters to a football match. The first train is full, but not the second. The ratio of the number carried by the first train to that carried by the second is 9 : 7. Find the number carried in each train.
For the return journey 120 supporters fail to catch either train, but the first train to depart is again full. Find the ratio of the numbers travelling on each train for the return journey.

12 🖩 The ratio of the length, width and height of this parcel is 7 : 5 : 4. Find each of the three dimensions if the total length of fastening tape is 2 m.

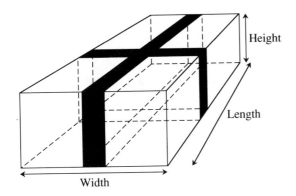

4.3 Squares and square roots

Activity 10

In this Activity we explore the relationship between the side length of a square and its area, and vice versa.

1   In the diagram the side length of the smallest square represents 1 cm.

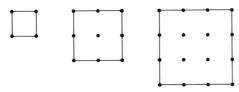

[W]   Area of smallest square

[W] $= 1 \times 1 \, cm^2$

[A] $= 1^2 \, cm^2 = 1 \, cm^2$

a Copy and complete this table:

Square	
Side length (cm)	Area (cm²)
1	$1 \times 1 = 1^2 = 1$
2	$2 \times 2 = 2^2 = 4$
3	
4	
5	
6	

b 'Three squared' is written 3^2. Write the following in a similar way:

(i) 'Eight squared'. (ii) 'Twelve squared'.
(iii) 'Two point six squared'. (iv) 'Nought point nine squared'.

c Work out the area of a square which has a side length of each of the following:
(i) 14 cm   (ii) 7.2 cm   (iii) 19 m   (iv) 0.74 m   (v) 120 m   (vi) 67.1 m

2   If we are given the area of a square we can find its side length. To do this we 'square root' the area. This means that we must find the number which, when multiplied by itself, gives the area.

For example, given a square of area 36 cm², the working is:

[W]   Side length of square

[W] $= \sqrt{36}$ cm   ⟵ This means the 'square root of 36'.

[A] $= 6$ cm

a Copy and complete this table:

Square	
Area (cm²)	Side length (cm)
36	$\sqrt{36} = 6$
49	
64	
81	
100	

b The 'square root of 36' is written $\sqrt{36}$. Write the following in a similar way:

(i) 'Square root of 200'. (ii) 'Square root of 2.4'.
(iii) 'Square root of 0.8'. (iv) 'Square root of 1 million'.

REMEMBER

- The 'square of 6' $= 6^2 = 36$.
- The 'square root of 36' $= \sqrt{36} = 6$.

— Revision Exercise 4A

Calculators are **not allowed**.

1 Change to a percentage: **a** $\frac{1}{2}$ **b** $\frac{3}{25}$ **c** $\frac{2}{5}$
2 Change to a fraction in its lowest terms: **a** 40% **b** 65% **c** 26%
3 Work out: **a** 10% of £45 **b** 15% of 600 km **c** 34% of 30 kg
4 Write 18 cm as a percentage of 20 cm.
5

120 g	105 g
Before	After

    a What fraction of the original weight has been lost?
    b What is this as a percentage?
6 Mrs Richards divides £30 between David and Denise in the ratio 3 : 2. How much does each receive?
7 There are 280 boys and 350 girls in a school. Find the ratio of boys to girls.
8 Work out: **a** 8^2 **b** 13^2 **c** $\sqrt{144}$ **d** $\sqrt{400}$
9 The diagram represents a square flower bed.
   Find the length of one side.

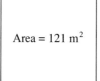

Area = 121 m^2

— Revision Exercise 4B

Calculators are **not allowed**.

1 Change to a percentage: **a** $\frac{3}{20}$ **b** $\frac{3}{16}$ **c** 0.95
2 Change to a fraction in its lowest terms: **a** 85% **b** 2.5% **c** 0.5%
3 Work out: **a** 36% of £40 **b** 1% of 100 000 km **c** 0.1% of 50 000 tonnes
4 Write 60 cm as a percentage of 3 m.
5 Jane throws the javelin for her school. At the beginning of the season she threw 40 m. By the end of the season her best throw was 43 m. What was her improvement, as a percentage?
6 An exam is marked out of 60. Eight pupils sit the exam and their marks are:
    48 44 40 34 28 26 25 24
   If 45% is a pass, how many failed?
7 A father divides £72 between his three daughters in the ratio 3 : 4 : 5. How much does each receive?
8 A mother gives her three sons their pocket money in the ratio of their ages. The amounts are:
    £4.90 £7.70 £8.40
   If the oldest is twelve years old, how old are the other two?
9 Work out: **a** $(1.3)^2$ **b** $\sqrt{225}$ **c** $\sqrt{1.44}$

Basics Test 4

A Calculator

Write each answer to the nearest tenth.

1 $49.7 - 65.09 + 2.98$

2 $0.487 \div 0.0784$

3 0.689^2

4 $\frac{5}{9}$ of 2.08

5 $\frac{3.04 \times 2.97}{1.31}$

6 $\frac{3.04 - 2.97}{1.31}$

B Paper and pencil

7 $207 + 48 + 56 + 94$

8 $9.2 + 0.765 - 5.987$

9 2.24×2.9

10 $1155 \div 21$

11 $\frac{5}{6} - \frac{3}{4}$

12 $\frac{5}{6} \times \frac{3}{4}$

13 What is 45% of 600 cm?

14 Write £96 as a fraction of £256 in its lowest terms

15 Estimate $480.9 \div 19$.

C Mental

Ten questions will be read out to you.

Puzzlers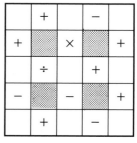

1 John says, 'Gill is not telling the truth.' Paul says, 'John is a liar.' Mark says, 'John is telling the truth.' Gill says, 'Paul and Mark are not both lying.' Who is telling the truth?

2 In the crossnumber (similar to a crossword) the nine blank spaces must be filled by the digits 1, 2, 3, 4, 5, 6, 7, 8 or 9 so that each row and each column equals 10.

a There are four different combinations of signs in the crossnumber. One of these is:

$$\square + \square - \square = 10$$

Write down the other three combinations.

b The combination $\square + \square + \square = 10$ can be completed in four different ways. Copy and complete the following (remember, you may not use the same digit more than once in each case):

$\boxed{7} + \boxed{2} + \square = 10$ $\boxed{6} + \square + \square = 10$

$\boxed{5} + \square + \square = 10$ $\boxed{5} + \square + \square = 10$

c Write down all the different ways in which the other three combinations you wrote down can be completed.

d Copy the crossnumber and use your answers to parts **b** and **c** to complete it.

Coursework: Athletics match

Four teams compete in an athletics match. The total points for each team have been worked out, except for the results for the discus, which is the last event. Which team wins and which team could have won?

1 The points scoring system for each event is shown in Table 1.

Position	1st	2nd	3rd	4th	5th	6th	7th	8th
Points	9	7	6	5	4	3	2	1

Table 1

Table 2 shows the partially completed results sheet for the discus event, showing the distance thrown by each of the eight competitors in each of their three throws in the competition. Copy and complete this results sheet.

Name	Team	Distance thrown (m)			Best throw	Position	Points
		First	Second	Third			
Andrew	A	23.45	23.36	23.44			
Bert	B	27.89	25.08	27.75			
Carl	C	29.74	27.75	29.76			
David	D	25.34	25.90	23.58			
Albert	A	26.86	29.77	29.51			
Bruce	B	21.42	20.87	21.46			
Chris	C	23.34	22.98	23.54			
Don	D	24.87	24.56	24.01			

Table 2

2 The total points for all the events in the match *except* the discus are shown in Table 3. Use the results of the discus competition to work out the points and positions for each team in the whole match.

Team	A	B	C	D
Total points (excluding discus)	109	118	85	124

Table 3

EXTENSION

3 a If Bruce had finished second in the discus competition instead of eighth, work out the new total points for each team for the whole match. (All other competitors, except the winner, finish one place down.)

b Would it have been possible for either team A or team B to have won the match, if their discus throwers had performed better?

73

5 ALGEBRA I

5.1 Substitution

In mathematics we can use letters to represent numbers. For example, '$a + b$' means that if we are told the numbers which 'a' and 'b' represent, then we should add them together.

In English we know the meaning of the word 'cat', but in mathematics, when the letters represent numbers, 'cat' is called an 'expression' and means $c \times a \times t$.

■ EXAMPLE 1

If $c = 3$, $a = 4.2$ and $t = 9$, find the value of cat.

Facts [F]	$c = 3$, $a = 4.2$, $t = 9$
Expression [E]	$c \times a \times t$
Substitution [S]	$= 3 \times 4.2 \times 9$
Working [W]	$cat = 113.4$

REMEMBER

cat means $c \times a \times t$.

$$\begin{array}{r} 4.2 \\ \times 3 \\ \hline 12.6 \\ \times 9 \\ \hline 113.4 \end{array}$$

Notice how we set out the question. First we put down the facts [F], followed by the expression [E]; then we substitute [S] the facts into the expression, do any working [W] and then finally give the answer .

To help you to remember the four stages involved, try to make up a mnemonic, for example, 'Fred Eats Squashed Wombats'.

■ EXAMPLE 2

If $x = 5.3$, $y = 2.1$ and $z = 12.6$, find the value of $x + y + z$.

[F]	$x = 5.3$, $y = 2.1$, $z = 12.6$
[E]	$x + y + z$
[S]	$= 5.3 + 2.1 + 12.6$
[W]	$= 20.0$ (or 20)

$$\begin{array}{r} 5.3 \\ 2.1 \\ + 12.6 \\ \hline 20.0 \end{array}$$

■ EXAMPLE 3

If $m = 1$, and $n = 8$, find the value of $\frac{m}{n}$ as a decimal.

[F]	$m = 1$, $n = 8$
[E]	$\frac{m}{n}$ (or $m \div n$)
[S]	$= \frac{1}{8}$ (or $1 \div 8$)
[W]	$= 0.125$

REMEMBER

$\frac{m}{n}$ means m divided by n.

$$8\overline{\smash{\big)}\,1.000}$$
$$0.125$$

74

___ Exercise 28

1 If $p = 63$, $q = 21$ and $r = 3$, find the value of:

a $p + q + r$ **b** $\frac{p}{q}$ **c** $\frac{p}{r}$

d $\frac{q}{r}$ **e** pr **f** qr

2 If $t = 48$, $u = 12$ and $v = 36$, find the value of:

a $t + u - v$ **b** $\frac{v}{u}$ **c** $\frac{v}{t}$

d $\frac{u}{t}$ **e** tu **f** tv

3 If $m = 4$, $n = 12$ and $p = 2$, find the value of:

a np **b** $\frac{np}{m}$ **c** mpn

d $mn + mp$ **e** $mn + np$ **f** $mp + np$

4 Find the difference between each of the following if $x = 9$ and $y = 6$:

a xy and $x + y$ **b** xy and $x - y$ **c** xy and $\frac{x}{y}$

d $x + y$ and $x - y$ **e** $x + y$ and $\frac{x}{y}$ **f** $x - y$ and $\frac{x}{y}$

5 Find the difference between each of the following if $u = 0.6$ and $v = 0.2$:

a $\frac{u}{v}$ and $u - v$ **b** $\frac{u}{v}$ and $u + v$ **c** $\frac{u}{v}$ and uv

d $u + v$ and $u - v$ **e** $u + v$ and uv **f** $u - v$ and uv

6 Find the value of each of the following if $p = 2.5$, $q = 1.5$ and $r = 4.5$:

a $p + p$ **b** $q + q + q$ **c** $r + r + r + r$

d $p + p - q$ **e** $p + p - r$ **f** $q + q + q - p$

MASTERMINDER

7 If $t = 17$ and $s = 34$, find the value of:

a $\frac{t}{s} \times \frac{t}{s} \times \frac{t}{s} \times \frac{t}{s} \times \frac{t}{s} \times \frac{t}{s}$ **b** $\frac{t \times t \times t \times t \times t \times t}{s \times s \times s \times s \times s \times s}$

c $\frac{t}{s} + \frac{t}{s} + \frac{t}{s} + \frac{t}{s} + \frac{t}{s} + \frac{t}{s}$ **d** $\frac{t + t + t + t + t + t}{s + s + s + s + s + s}$

Use your calculator to check each answer.

> ___ *NOTE*
>
> When a number and a letter are multiplied together,
> the number is always written first, thus:
> $2e$ means $2 \times e$.

■ *EXAMPLE 4*

Find the value of $3r$ if $r = 94$.

[F] $r = 94$

[E] $3r$

[S] $= 3 \times 94$

[W] $= 282$

$$\begin{array}{r} 94 \\ \times\ \ 3 \\ \hline 282 \end{array}$$

▬ Exercise 29

1   If $p = 4$ and $q = 3$, find the value of:
  a $2p$ **b** $8q$ **c** $3pq$
  d $3p + q$ **e** $10p - q$ **f** $4q - p$

2   If $u = 5$ and $v = 6$, find the value of:
  a $2u$ **b** $9v$ **c** $8uv$
  d $4u + 3v$ **e** $5v - 3u$ **f** $\frac{1}{2}u + v$

3   If $x = 6$ and $y = 0.2$, find the value of:
  a $3y$ **b** $2xy$ **c** $x - 2y$
  d $4x + 5y$ **e** $0.1x + y$ **f** $\frac{1}{2}x + \frac{1}{2}y$

4   Find the difference between each of the following, if $m = 4$ and $n = 0.2$:
  a $3m$ and $2n$ **b** $4n$ and $0.2m$ **c** $10m$ and $10n$
  d $\frac{1}{2}m$ and n **e** m and $0.1n$ **f** $\frac{1}{4}m$ and $\frac{1}{2}n$

5   Find the value of each of the following if $r = \frac{1}{2}$ and $s = \frac{1}{4}$:
  a $4r$ **b** $8s$ **c** $2rs$
  d $3r - s$ **e** $5r - 2s$ **f** $\frac{1}{2}r + 4s$

6   Find the value of each of the following if $t = 4.2$, $u = 2.4$ and $v = 0.5$:
  a $6t$ **b** $9u$ **c** $10tv$
  d $6t + 9u$ **e** $6t - 9u$ **f** $0.4uv$

MASTERMINDER

7   Find the value of the expression:

$$\frac{7s}{s + s + s + s + s + s + s}$$

when **a** $s = 5$ **b** $s = 7$ **c** $s = 5.7$.

Comment on your answers.

___ *Activity 11*

A train leaves London on a 99-mile journey to Leicester. (The numbers on the diagram represent the distances between stations in miles.)

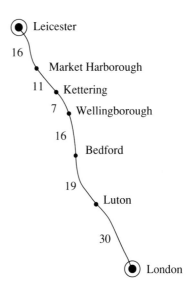

The train travels 39 miles. The distance it will be from Leicester
= (99 − 39) miles
= 60 miles

The train travels x miles. The distance it will be from Leicester
= (99 − x) miles

Notice that, for this problem, (99 − x) is the **expression** which, when we **substitute** a value for x, will give the distance in miles from Leicester.

For example, find the distance of the train from Leicester after it has travelled 35 miles.

[F] $x = 35$

[E]   (99 − x) miles

[S]   = (99 − 35) miles

[W]   = 64 miles

Copy and complete this table:

Could x represent numbers larger than 99? What about negative numbers? Comment and, if possible, give an example of each.

Value of x	Distance in miles from Leicester	Nearest station
35	99 − 35 = 64	Luton
45		
55		
65		
75		
85		

___ Exercise 30

1   The perimeter of a square is four times the length of one side. Copy and complete:

Find the perimeter when $x = 9$.

Length of one side	Perimeter
8 cm	4 × 8 = 32 cm
12 cm	
16 cm	
x cm	

2   A bicycle is bought for £100. When it is sold a profit is made. Copy and complete:

Find the profit when $x = 105$.

Selling price	Profit
£120	120 − 100 = £20
£145	
£x	

3 A calculator is bought for £16. When it is sold a loss is made. Copy and complete:

Find the loss when $x = 8$.

Selling price	Loss
£12	
£9	
£x	

4 A mother was 32 years old when she gave birth to John. Copy and complete:

When $x = 47$, what is John's age?

Mother's age	John's age
34 years	
38 years	
x years	

5 A mother was 26 years old when she gave birth to Joan. Copy and complete:

When $y = 17$, what is the mother's age?

Joan's age	Mother's age
6 years	
13 years	
y years	

6 A new 5-mile bypass is being constructed. Copy and complete:

When $x = 28$, find the length completed.

% completed	Length completed
5	
70	
x	

7 Nelson's Column is 60 m high. Copy and complete the table to show how many times higher the four buildings are than Nelson's Column.

If $x = 410$, representing the height of the Empire State Building, approximately how many times higher is it than Nelson's Column?

Building	Height (to nearest m)	Number of of times higher[*]
St Paul's Cathedral	110	
Telecom Tower	190	
Eiffel Tower	320	
Any building	x	

* to the nearest whole number.

8 The maximum number of identical stamps is bought for £10. Copy and complete:

When $x = 4$, how many can be bought?

Cost of each stamp	Number bought
25p	
80p	
xp	

9 A car uses five litres of petrol to travel 60 km. Write down an expression to give the distance travelled using y litres of petrol.

MASTERMINDERS

10 The fuel consumption of a coach is 24 mpg. Write down an expression to give the fuel used on a journey of m miles.

11 Mr Speed competes in a 20-mile powerboat race. Copy and complete:

When $x = 80$, find the distance to be completed.

% travelled	Distance to be completed
10	
45	
x	

12 A magic box will always do the same to any term put into it. If 1 is put in, the number 7 will be produced.

$$1 \quad \rightarrow \quad \boxed{\text{Magic box}} \quad \rightarrow \quad 7$$

The table shows the result of putting each of three numbers into the magic box. Copy and complete the table.

Number put in	Number produced
1	7
2	10
3	13
x	
9	

__ 5.2 Addition and subtraction

Only 'like terms' can be added or subtracted. Look at the following examples.

1 2 cows + 7 cows = 9 cows

2 2 cows + 3 sheep + 4 sheep = 2 cows + 7 sheep

3 10 pins + 6 nails − 3 pins = 7 pins + 6 nails

4 £3 + 60p + £4 + 75p   (Change pounds to pence)

= 300p + 60p + 400p + 75p

= 835p

5 £3 + 60p + £4 + 75p   (Change pence to pounds)

= £3 + £0.60 + £4 + £0.75

= £8.35

6 $\frac{2}{3} - \frac{1}{2}$ (Change both fractions to sixths)

$= \frac{4}{6} - \frac{3}{6} = \frac{1}{6}$

When adding and subtracting letters in algebra, the same rule applies.

5 ALGEBRA I

■ EXAMPLE 1

a $2a + 4a + 3a = 9a$

b $10p + 6p - 3p = 13p$

c $\dfrac{a}{5} + \dfrac{a}{5} = \dfrac{2a}{5}$

d $12ab + 13ab + 14ab = 39ab$

e $\dfrac{5}{a} - \dfrac{3}{a} = \dfrac{2}{a}$

REMEMBER

[W] Words

[W] Working

[A] Answer

■ EXAMPLE 2

David walks $3x$ miles followed by $6x$ miles and then $4x$ miles. Find the total distance walked.

[W]   Total distance walked

[W] $= (3x + 6x + 4x)$ miles

[A] $= 13x$ miles

■ EXAMPLE 3

A bookseller buys a book for £$12a$ and eventually sells it for £$9a$. How much does he lose in the sale?

[W]   Loss

[W] $= £12a - £9a$

[A] $= £3a$

Remember to set out the questions in the following exercises exactly as these examples have been set out.

___ Exercise 31

In Questions 1 to 12, simplify the expression.

1 $3x + 4x + 5x$

2 $5t + 7t - 2t$

3 $2y + 4y + 6y - 8y$

4 $3rs + 5rs + 16rs - 4rs$

5 $21a - 4a + 3a - a$

6 $4u + 5u - u - 3u$

7 $8v - 3v - 2v - v$

8 $8ab - 5ab - ab$

9 $\frac{1}{9} + \frac{4}{9} + \frac{2}{9} - \frac{5}{9}$

10 $\frac{21x}{25} - \frac{9x}{25} - \frac{6x}{25}$

11 $\frac{12}{b} - \frac{4}{b} - \frac{5}{b}$

12 $\frac{25}{n} - \frac{7}{n} - \frac{13}{n}$

13 In a test Helen got the following marks: $5t$, $2t$ and $3t$. What was her total?

14 The table shows the numbers of three types of book in a library. What is the total number of books?

Type of book	Number of books
Fiction	$17u$
Reference	$5u$
Biography	$13u$

15 Ben walked for the following numbers of kilometres: $3v$, $9v$ and $8v$. How far did he walk altogether?

16 A fruit shop has $10r$ oranges to sell. After selling $4r$ oranges, how many are left?

17 A piece of string is $23g$ metres long. $12g$ metres are cut off. How much remains?

18 Railway platform tickets cost b pence each. How much do seven tickets cost ?

MASTERMINDERS

19 Phil and Chris run in the same race. Phil takes t minutes and Chris takes t seconds less. How long does Chris take?

20 A small garden plot is surrounded by four large concrete slabs.

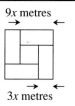

9x metres

a Find, in terms of x, the total distance around (i) the outer edge of the slabs, and (ii) the inner edge of the slabs.

b Find the value of x if the distance around the outer edge is 6 m greater than that around the inner edge.

3x metres

21 Liam can use either of the two routes shown for cycling to school.

a If all the distances shown are in metres and the two routes are the same length, write down the route length in terms of both a and b.

b If the distance-meter on Liam's bicycle tells him that the route length is between 300 and 400 metres, find the value of both a and b.

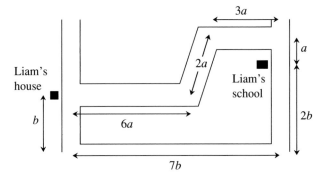

■ EXAMPLE 4

Simplify $4r + 3s + 9r - 2s - 13r$.

Re-arrange the expression: (Write r terms together.)   (Write s terms together.)

$$4r + 3s + 9r - 2s - 13r \quad = 4r + 9r - 13r + 3s - 2s$$

$$= 13r - 13r + s$$

$$= s$$

⎯ Exercise 32

In Questions 1 to 15, simplify the expression.

1 $3a + 6b + 2a + 3b$

2 $5x + 3y + 2x + 9y + 4x$

3 $4c + 8d + 2c + 2d + c + 5d$

4 $2m + 11n + 9m + 2n - 5m$

5 $10u + v + 5u + 7v - 6u$

6 $8b + 5c - 4b + 2c + 11b + 4c$

7 $12r + 7s - 3r + 11s - 4r$

8 $11y + 9z - 7y + 6z - 3y$

9 $7q + 25r + 9q - 18r + 8q$

10 $5m + 28n + 12m - 19n + 3m$

11 $6x + 21y + 10x - 16y - 13x$

12 $4z + 19t + 18z - 11t - 21z$

13 $9ab + 20cd - 2ab - 9cd + 18ab$

14 $25pq + 15rs - 8pq - 14rs - 9pq$

15 $22u + 29v - 13u - 13v - 9u$

16 Find the perimeter of this shape.
(All dimensions are in cm.)

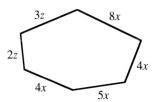

17 Fuad has £$76y$ in his savings account. He withdraws the following amounts: £$14y$, £$17y$, £$21c$, £$9c$. How much does he have left?

18 The diagram represents four motorway exits, A, B, C and D. What is the distance between exits C and D? (All distances are in km.)

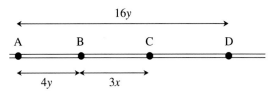

19 Ebrahim has £$63x$ in his savings account. His deposits and withdrawals in one week are shown in this table:

How much was in his account at the end of the week?

Day	Deposit	Withdrawal
Monday	£$9x$	
Tuesday		£$12x$
Wednesday		£$17y$
Thursday	£$9y$	
Friday	£$21y$	
Saturday		£$7x$

MASTERMINDER

20 The diagram shows two routes from London to Nottingham. Write down, in terms of a and b, the distance by each of the two routes. All dimensions are in kilometres.

If the distance is 195 km by either route and Peterborough is midway between Nottingham and Hitchin, find the value of both a and b, given that both numbers end with a five.

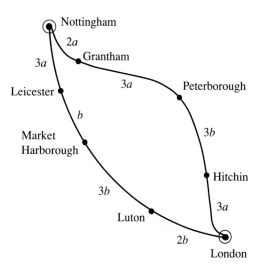

83

▬ 5.3 Equations

▬ *Activity 12*

A savings account gives a very good example of how simple equations can be used in practice. Suppose you have a savings account. When you **deposit** a sum of money, you add money to your account. When you **withdraw** a sum of money, you take money away from your account. The money in your account after a deposit or a withdrawal is known as the **balance**.

A **deposit** means that money is **added** to the account.

A **withdrawal** means that money is **taken away** from the account.

The **balance** is the **result** after a deposit or withdrawal.

Look carefully at the three examples and you will see how a simple equation can represent a deposit or a withdrawal.

■ *EXAMPLE 1*

Manhar has £20 in his account. He deposits £4 and makes his balance equal to £a. How much is then in his account?

From the above, £20 + £4 = £a.

$$\text{Therefore } a = 24.$$

■ *EXAMPLE 2*

Jill has £16 in her account. She deposits a certain amount of money (£b) and makes her balance equal to £20. How much did she deposit?

From the above, £16 + £b = £20.

$$\text{Therefore } b = 4.$$

■ *EXAMPLE 3*

Robert has £c in his account, and he withdraws £6 which makes his balance equal to £13. Find how much he had in his account.

From the above, £c−£6 = £13.

$$\text{Therefore } c = 19.$$

The answers to these three examples are numbers 1 to 3 in the table opposite. Copy and complete the table, which tells the 'stories' of 24 different savings-account transactions.

	Initial amount	Withdrawal	Deposit	Balance	Equation of the 'story'	Answer to the 'story'
1	20		4	a	$20 + 4 = a$	Balance (a) = 24
2	16		b	20	$16 + b = 20$	Deposit (b) = 4
3	c	6		13	$c - 6 = 13$	Amount (c) = 19
4	4.95	3.45		d		
5	8.25		n	9.75		
6	27.50	q		16.25		
7	x		8	13		
8	y		4.57	5.89		
9	t	8.46		3.69		
10					$6 + 9 = r$	
11					$17 - 8 = s$	
12					$7 + t = 15$	
13					$29 - u = 24$	
14	35		13			Balance (x) =
15	41	16				Balance (y) =
16	12			21		Deposit (a) =
17	35			19		Withdrawal (b) =
18			13	16		Amount (c) =
19		14		17		Amount (d) =
20	12				= 14	Deposit (m) =
21	39				= 27	Withdrawal (n) =
22			3.15		= 12.50	Amount (p) =
23			5.35		= 20	Amount (q) =
24		7.74			= 7.26	Amount (r) =

You should have noticed three different types of equation in the last Activity. We shall use a mathematical method to solve each of the following types:

$$9 + x = 16 \quad \text{[i]}$$

$$-9 + x = 4 \quad \text{[ii]}$$

$$9 - x = 4 \quad \text{[iii]}$$

The principle is to **cancel** out the letter or number by doing the **same to both sides** of the equation. Look carefully at the examples.

■ *EXAMPLE 4*

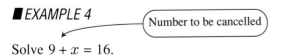
Number to be cancelled

Solve $9 + x = 16$.

Subtract 9 from both sides.

$$- \cancel{9} + \cancel{9} + x = 16 - 9$$

$$x = 7$$

85

■ *EXAMPLE 5*

Number to be cancelled

Solve $-9 + x = 4$.

Add 9 to both sides.
$$\cancel{9} - \cancel{9} + x = 4 + 9$$
$$x = 13$$

■ *EXAMPLE 6*

Letter to be cancelled

Solve $9 - x = 4$.

Add x to both sides.
$$9 - \cancel{x} + \cancel{x} = x + 4$$

Subtract 4 from both sides.
$$9 - 4 = x + \cancel{4} - \cancel{4}$$
$$5 = x$$
$$x = 5$$

REMEMBER

There is only **one rule**: you must do the **same operation to both sides**.

Flow diagram 1 will help you understand the process more clearly. Use it when doing the next Exercise.

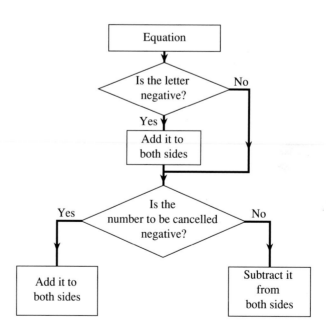

Flow diagram 1

___ Exercise 33

Solve each equation using the method in Flow diagram 1.

1 $x + 5 = 21$ **2** $y + 6 = 12$ **3** $23 = z + 11$ **4** $t + 7 = 7$

5 $u + 0 = 6$ **6** $5 + a = 8$ **7** $19 = 6 + b$ **8** $9 + c = 10$

9 $m - 3 = 7$ **10** $n - 9 = 4$ **11** $8 = p - 4$ **12** $q - 13 = 13$

13 $r + 19 = 0$ **14** $s - 0 = 9$ **15** $5 - x = 3$ **16** $12 + y = 5$

17 $10 - z = 1$ **18** $6 = 7 - t$ **19** $9 - u = 0$ **20** $8 - v = 8$

MASTERMINDERS

21 $21.6 + t = 9.6$ **22** $y - \frac{3}{8} = \frac{4}{5}$ **23** $0.076 = 0.01 - r$ **24** $\frac{5}{8} = 0.0123 - w$

There are three other types of equation which you must be able to solve. The same principle applies; that is, you must do **the same to both sides** to cancel out a letter or a number. Examples of these types of equations are:

$$9x = 36 \quad \text{[iv]}$$

$$\frac{x}{9} = 6 \quad \text{[v]}$$

$$\frac{9}{x} = 2 \quad \text{[vi]}$$

> *REMEMBER*
>
> $9x$ means 9 times x.
>
> $\frac{x}{9}$ means x divided by 9.

■*EXAMPLE 7*   (Number to be cancelled)

Solve $9x = 36$.

Divide both sides by 9.

$$\frac{\cancel{9}x}{\cancel{9}} = \frac{36}{9}$$

$$x = 4$$

■ *EXAMPLE 8*

Solve $\dfrac{x}{9} = 6$.

> Number to be cancelled

Multiply both sides by 9.

$$\cancel{9} \times \dfrac{x}{\cancel{9}} = 6 \times 9$$

$$x = 54$$

■ *EXAMPLE 9*

Solve $\dfrac{9}{x} = 2$.

> Letter to be cancelled

Multiply both sides by x.

$$\cancel{x} \times \dfrac{9}{\cancel{x}} = 2 \times x$$

$$9 = 2 \times x$$

Divide both sides by 2.

$$\dfrac{9}{2} = \dfrac{\cancel{2} \times x}{\cancel{2}}$$

$$x = 4.5$$

Flow diagram 2 will help you understand the process more clearly. Use it when doing the next Exercise.

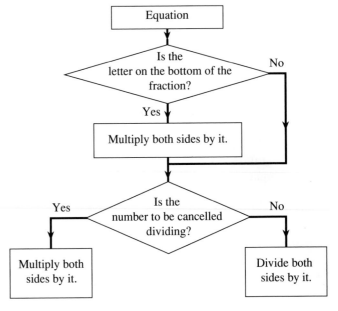

Flow diagram 2

___ Exercise 34

Solve each equation using the method in Flow diagram 2.

1 $3x = 12$	**2** $5y = 35$	**3** $11z = 33$	**4** $98 = 7t$
5 $120 = 8u$	**6** $12v = 156$	**7** $\frac{a}{3} = 4$	**8** $\frac{b}{8} = 5$
9 $\frac{c}{9} = 9$	**10** $14 = \frac{d}{2}$	**11** $45 = \frac{m}{3}$	**12** $\frac{n}{11} = 33$
13 $\frac{p}{3} = 0$	**14** $2x = 14$	**15** $25w = 0$	**16** $\frac{12}{x} = 4$
17 $\frac{18}{y} = 9$	**18** $7 = \frac{35}{z}$	**19** $13 = \frac{78}{t}$	**20** $\frac{600}{u} = 12$

MASTERMINDERS

21 $3.4z = 25.5$	**22** $x \div 9.7 = 7.9$	**23** $0.45 = \frac{0.27}{y}$	**24** $\frac{4}{9} = \frac{22}{-e}$

▬ Revision Exercise 5A

Calculators are **not allowed**.

1   If $a = 2$ and $b = 4$, find the value of:
   a $a + b$ **b** $3b$ **c** $\frac{b}{a}$ **d** $b + a + b + a$

2   A compact disc player is bought for £400.
   When it is sold a loss is made. Copy and
   complete this table:

Selling price	Loss
£350	
£300	
£x	

   Find the loss when $x = 325$.

3   Simplify: **a** $2x + 2x + 2x$ **b** $3y - 2y$ **c** $5t + 5t - 4t$ **d** $4a + 2a - a$
4   Joyce and Jane run in the same race. Joyce takes t minutes and Jane takes s minutes longer.
   How long does Jane take?
5   Solve for x: **a** $12x = 48$ **b** $12 + x = 48$ **c** $x - 12 = 48$ **d** $\frac{x}{12} = 48$
6   A cinema ticket costs r pounds. How much do five tickets cost?
7   Simplify: **a** $2x + 2x + 2y$ **b** $a + b + a + b$ **c** $3x - 2x + 3y$ **d** $2x + 2y - y$
8   If $x = 2$, $y = 3$ and $z = 4$, find the value of:
   a $x + y - z$ **b** $xy + z$ **c** $\frac{xy}{z}$ **d** $yz - xy$
9   Solve for x: **a** $21 = \frac{x}{7}$ **b** $21 = x - 7$ **c** $21 = 7 + x$ **d** $21 = \frac{7}{x}$

▬ Revision Exercise 5B

Calculators are **not allowed**.

1   If $a = 5$ and $b = 4$, find the value of:
   a $a + a + a$ **b** $a - b + a$ **c** $2ab$ **d** $\frac{ab}{a}$

2   A mother was 27 years old when she gave birth
   to Ingrid. Copy and complete this table:

Mother's age	Ingrid's age
30 years	
38 years	
x years	

   When $x = 42$, what was Ingrid's age?

3   Simplify: **a** $a + a + a$ **b** $a - b + a$ **c** $3x + 2x - 2x$ **d** $4b - 3b + 2b - b$
4   Marcus goes shopping with £$9a$. He spends £a on books, £$4a$ on records and £$3a$ on stationery.
   How much does he have left?
5   Solve for x: **a** $9x = 108$ **b** $10 + x = 12.5$ **c** $\frac{x}{9} = 108$ **d** $x - 4.5 = 4.5$
6   A cinema ticket costs b pounds. How much do x tickets cost?
7   Simplify: **a** $5t + 6s + 5t - t$ **b** $6a + 7b - 3a - 3b$ **c** $9y - y - x - y$ **d** $16t - 15d + 6t$
8   If $x = 2$ and $y = 0.4$, find the value of:
   a $3xy$ **b** $y + y + y + x$ **c** $\frac{10y}{x}$ **d** $xy - yx$
9   Solve for x: **a** $18 = 4.5 + x$ **b** $4.5 = 18 - x$ **c** $18 = \frac{x}{4.5}$ **d** $18 = \frac{4.5}{x}$

Basics Test 5

A Calculator

Write each answer to the nearest hundred.

1 $298.4 - 876$

2 $68 \text{ million} \div 48\,200$

3 $68 \times 74 \times 9.6$

4 58.9^2

5 Solve for x: $6x = 9432$

6 Solve for y: $\frac{y}{9} = 482$

B Paper and pencil

7 $2.0057 - 1.9688$

8 Simplify: $2a + 3b + 6a - 2b$

9 When $a = 4.9$ and $b = 9.4$, what is the value of ab?

10 When $c = 896$ and $d = 32$, what is the value of $c \div d$?

11 $\sqrt{256}$

12 $\frac{11}{12} + \frac{3}{20}$

13 What is 1% of £6000?

14 Write £108 as a percentage of £450.

15 Change 0.09 km to metres.

C Mental

Ten questions will be read out to you. Use the following facts to answer Questions 16 to 20:

$a = 2, \quad b = 3, \quad c = 7$

Puzzlers

1 An automatic toll (similar to the one at the Dartford Tunnel) accepts any combination of silver coins provided that the total is 60p. Find all the possible ways in which the toll can be paid.

2 Make an accurate drawing of each of these rectangles.

Draw a diagram to show how the 8 cm by 3 cm rectangle can be cut into two identical parts which will fit exactly to cover the 12 cm by 2 cm rectangle.

3 Here are two multiplication sums. If each letter represents a different digit, find the value of each of the letters.

a
```
      Y Z
  ×   Y Z
  ───────
    X Y Z
```

b
```
      P Q
  ×   P R
  ───────
    Q R R
```

Coursework: Finding the mass

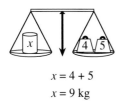

$x = 4 + 5$
$x = 9 \text{ kg}$

Figure 1

The aim is to find the mass of a bag of sugar by using an old-fashioned beam balance and any number of weights of mass 4 kg and 5 kg.

In each calculation we let the mass of the bag of sugar be x kg. An equation is made which is then solved to find the value of x.

1 In Figure 1 the mass of the bag of sugar (x) balances with the mass of the two weights. This shows that the mass of the bag of sugar is 9 kg.

Copy the three diagrams in Figure 2. In each case complete the equation and solve it to find the mass of the bag of sugar.

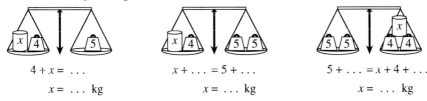

$4 + x = \ldots$ $x + \ldots = 5 + \ldots$ $5 + \ldots = x + 4 + \ldots$
$x = \ldots \text{ kg}$ $x = \ldots \text{ kg}$ $x = \ldots \text{ kg}$

Figure 2

2 In part 1 you discovered how the masses of 9 kg, 1 kg, 6 kg and 2 kg bags of sugar could be found. The results are entered in the table below. By using the **least** number of 4 kg and 5 kg weights, show how the masses of the other six bags could be found. Copy and complete the table.

Lefthand side	Righthand side	Mass of sugar (x)	Lefthand side	Righthand side	Mass of sugar (x)
x =	$4 + 5$	9 kg	=		5 kg
$x + 4$ =	5	1 kg	=		10 kg
$x + 4$ =	$5 + 5$	6 kg	=		8 kg
$5 + 5$ =	$x + 4 + 4$	2 kg	=		3 kg
=		4 kg	=		7 kg

3 A bag of sugar is placed on the lefthand side of the balance together with three 4 kg weights. This balances with five 5 kg weights. Write down the equation to show this and solve it to find the mass of the bag of sugar.

4 Six bags of sugar, of equal mass, are placed on the lefthand side and balanced with twelve 5 kg weights. Write down the equation to show this and solve it to find the mass of one bag of sugar.

EXTENSION

5 A bag of sugar, of mass 8 kg, is placed on the lefthand side of the balance together with a number of 4 kg weights. This is balanced on the righthand side by a number of 5 kg weights. If the number of weights of each size is between 10 and 20, find the number of each size. (There are two answers.)

6 STATISTICS AND PROBABILITY

__ 6.1 Bar charts

A bar chart is a useful way to represent data. Look carefully at the following examples.

> NOTE
>
> Statistics is the science of collecting, classifying and using numerical data.

■ EXAMPLE 1

The five languages spoken by the most people are:

Chinese	700 000 000
English	400 000 000
Russian	265 000 000
Spanish	240 000 000
Hindustani	230 000 000

This information is shown on the bar chart.

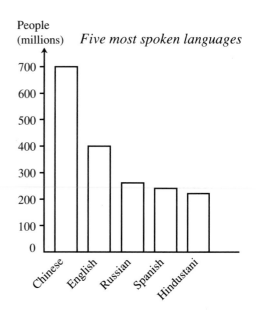

■ EXAMPLE 2

A car salesman recorded his sales for a certain week. The figures were as follows:

Monday 3 Tuesday 2 Wednesday 4
Thursday 1 Friday 2 Saturday 5

a Show these details on a bar chart.
b Work out what fraction of the total number of cars sold were sold each day. Convert each answer to a percentage. Comment on your answers.

a See the bar chart on the right.

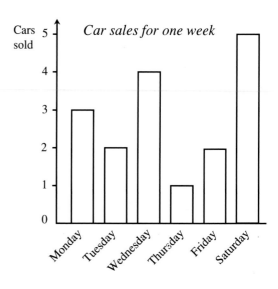

b [W]   Fraction of cars sold on Monday

[W], [A] $= \dfrac{3}{17}$

As a percentage, $\dfrac{3}{17} = \dfrac{3}{17} \times 100 = 18\%$ (to the nearest whole number)

The fractions and percentages for each day are shown in the table.

Day	Fraction	Percentage*
Monday	3/17	18%
Tuesday	2/17	12%
Wednesday	4/17	24%
Thursday	1/17	6%
Friday	2/17	12%
Saturday	5/17	29%

* to the nearest whole number.

The total of all the percentages is 101%. Had each percentage answer been written down accurately, the total would have been equal to 100%.

REMEMBER

- Give each bar chart a title.   • Label both axes clearly.

Tally marks

When collecting data it is often useful to use 'tally marks'. Numbers are written in groups of five, with the fifth number drawn through the first four, for example,

5 is written ⟍⟋⟋⟋⟋   6 is written ⟍⟋⟋⟋⟋ |

Writing numbers in this way makes it easier to count the totals.

Activity 13

Carry out a survey to find the method of transport used by each pupil in your class to get to school. Copy and complete this table to show your results.

a Draw a bar chart to illustrate your results.
b Work out for each of the methods what fraction of the total it was. Convert each fraction to a percentage, correct to the nearest whole number.

Method of transport	Tally marks	Totals
Bus		
Car		
Walk		
Bicycle		
Other		

___ Exercise 35

1 Draw a bar chart to display the facts in this table:

Top five honey-producing countries	
Country	Thousands of tonnes per year
USSR (former)	193
China	115
USA	82
Mexico	62
Argentina	34

2 Draw bar charts to display these facts.

a

Top five exporters of oil	
Country	Millions of tonnes per year
Saudi Arabia	168
USSR (former)	128
UK	80
Iran	78
Mexico	78

b

Top five importers of oil	
Country	Millions of tonnes per year
Japan	180
USA	172
France	70
W. Germany	70
Italy	67

3 Fifty boys were asked which sport they preferred to watch on TV, with these results.
   a Draw a bar chart to show these results.
   b Work out what fraction of the total preferred each sport. Change each answer to a percentage so that the results can be compared more easily.

Sport	Number of boys
Snooker	12
Soccer	18
Rugby	8
Athletics	6
Other	6

4 Fifty girls were asked which subject they enjoyed most. Here are the results.
   a Draw a bar chart to show these results.
   b Work out for each subject what fraction of the total it was. Change each fraction to a percentage.

Subject	Number of girls
English	15
Maths	12
French	10
Science	9
Other	4

5 A single die was rolled 50 times and the following scores were noted:

3, 1, 5, 6, 1,   2, 1, 2, 3, 2,
5, 2, 5, 1, 2,   4, 4, 6, 3, 5,
3, 1, 5, 4, 6,   2, 4, 4, 6, 3,
2, 6, 2, 5, 4,   6, 5, 4, 5, 6,
5, 4, 5, 2, 3,   1, 3, 3, 6, 1.

Copy the table and enter the results.
   a Draw a bar chart to show the results.
   b Which score occurred (i) least, (ii) most?
   c Are the results what you would expect?

Number	Tally marks	Totals
1		
2		
3		
4		
5		
6		
		50

MASTERMINDER

6   The table shows the numbers of goals scored by a school football team in twelve matches.

Number of goals	Number of matches in which they scored that number of goals
0	1
1	2
2	5
3	3
4	0
5	1

a Draw a bar chart to represent this information.

b Work out the total number of goals scored in the twelve matches.

___ Activity 14

Roll two dice 100 times and note the **total** of the two numbers for each throw. Tabulate your results and draw a bar chart to illustrate the information.

a   Which total(s) occurred (i) least, (ii) most?

b   Comment on the shape of your bar chart.

___ Activity 15

Count the number of people in each of 50 cars passing a certain place. Tabulate your results and draw a bar chart to illustrate the information.

a   Copy and complete the statement:

    'Half the cars had fewer than ... people in'.

b   Comment on the shape of your bar chart.

___ Activity 16

Carry out a survey to find out the favourite type of TV programme of 30 people of your own age group. Draw a bar chart to illustrate your findings and comment on the result. (Think carefully about the classification of programmes.)

___ Activity 17

Carry out a survey of your own choice. Think carefully about:

a   Exactly what you are trying to find out.

b   How you intend to obtain the necessary information (data).

Tabulate your results and draw a suitable bar chart.
Write down any conclusions from your survey.

__ 6.2 Means (averages)

In this section we shall find out how to find the **mean** (or 'average') of a set of values.

__ *Activity 18*

Suppose your school has played five matches and scored the following goals: 5, 3, 4, 0, 3. What is your mean goal-score per match?

> *NOTE*
>
> Mean goals per match = $\dfrac{\text{TOTAL goals in all the matches}}{\text{TOTAL number of matches played}}$

So in this case, mean goals per match = $\dfrac{5+3+4+0+3}{5} = 3.$

('Per' means 'divided by'. The phrase 'miles per hour' can be written as 'miles/hour' or as '$\frac{\text{miles}}{\text{hour}}$', just as a fraction, say three quarters, can be written as 3/4 or $\frac{3}{4}$.)

A similar method is used for other calculations of the mean. For example:

a   Mean speed (= mean distance per time) = $\dfrac{\text{TOTAL distance}}{\text{TOTAL time}}$

b   Mean temperature per day = $\dfrac{\text{TOTAL temperature for all the days}}{\text{TOTAL number of days}}$

Copy and complete:

1   Mean time per race $= \dfrac{\text{TOTAL} \ldots}{\text{TOTAL} \ldots}$

2   Mean height per pupil $= \dfrac{\text{TOTAL} \ldots}{\text{TOTAL} \ldots}$

3   Mean population per country $= \dfrac{\text{TOTAL} \ldots}{\text{TOTAL} \ldots}$

4   Mean mark per pupil $= \dfrac{\text{TOTAL} \ldots}{\text{TOTAL} \ldots}$

5   Mean mark per test $= \dfrac{\text{TOTAL} \ldots}{\text{TOTAL} \ldots}$

■ *EXAMPLE 1*

Mary throws two dice together six times over. Her results are shown here.

Find her mean score per throw.

[W]   Mean score per throw = $\dfrac{\text{TOTAL score}}{\text{TOTAL number of throws}}$

[W] $= \dfrac{7 + 4 + 7 + 7 + 8 + 3}{6}$

[A] $= 6$

■ *EXAMPLE 2*

Peter, Robert, Jacob and Charles run in a 4 by 400 metre relay and their times are:
Peter 1 min 5 s,   Robert 1 min 3 s,   Jacob 59 s,   Charles 1 min 1 s.
Work out the mean time per person.

[W]   Mean time per person = $\dfrac{\text{TOTAL time}}{\text{TOTAL number of competitors}}$

[W] $= \dfrac{65 + 63 + 59 + 61}{4}$ seconds

[A] $= 62$ seconds $= 1$ minute 2 seconds

■ *EXAMPLE 3*

This is a bar chart showing the maximum temperature, in °C, on each day in a week in July.
Work out the mean temperature per day for that week.

[W]   Mean temperature per day

$= \dfrac{\text{TOTAL temperature}}{\text{TOTAL number of days}}$

[W] $= \dfrac{19 + 23 + 23 + 24 + 19 + 19 + 20}{7}$ °C

[A] $= 21$ °C

July temperatures

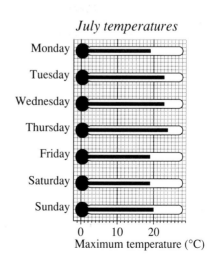

Exercise 36

1 Peter ran in the 100 m race for his school twelve times during the summer term. His times were as follows:

13.5 s,   14.0 s,   13.1 s,   13.6 s,
13.8 s,   14.1 s,   13.4 s,   13.7 s,
13.6 s,   13.9 s,   13.2 s,   13.3 s.

Find his mean time per race.

2 Emily fired eight arrows at a target which is shown here. Find her mean score per arrow.

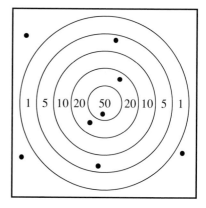

3 One year the children at Primrose Lane School recorded the number of wet days for each month. The details were as follows:

January	19	February	14	March	13
April	11	May	9	June	8
July	5	August	13	September	12
October	7	November	11	December	10

Find the mean number of wet days per month.

4 Mrs Gupta went to watch a tennis tournament which lasted four days. She travelled there and back by train each day. Here are details of her train fare and admission charges.

a Find the mean fare per day.
b Find the mean admission charge per day.

	Train fare	Admission charge
Friday	£12.50	£13.50
Saturday	£11.75	£13.50
Sunday	£11.20	£14.25
Monday	£11.75	£16.75

5 In the Jones family there are five children. The masses, heights and ages of the children are given in the table.

a Find the mean mass per child.
b Find the mean height per child.
c Find the mean age per child.

	Mass (kg)	Height (cm)	Age (years months)
Jean	55	157	15y 2m
Tom	49	158	13y 5m
Sally	36	149	10y 1m
Susan	31	119	7y 9m
David	19	104	4y 10m

6 Jane's mother has to drive a long way to work. One week her journey times were as follows:

Monday	1h 13 min	Tuesday	1h 18 min
Wednesday	1h 5 min	Thursday	56 min
Friday	58 min		

Find her mean journey time per day.

7 The timetable for trains from Aberdeen to Inverness is shown below.

| Aberdeen | 07:00 | 09:00 | 11:00 | 14:00 | 17:10 | 20:15 |
| Inverness | 09:30 | 11:25 | 13:24 | 16:35 | 19:40 | 22:45 |

Find the mean time per journey.

8 The bar chart shows the number of marks out of 10 gained by six pupils in a test.
a Find the girls' mean mark.
b Find the boys' mean mark.
c Find the overall mean mark.

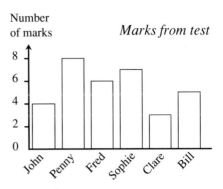

9 The number of peas in 50 pods were counted. The results are shown on the bar chart.
a Find the total number of peas.
b Find the mean number of peas per pod.

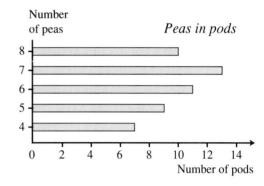

10 A survey was taken to find out the number of people living in each of 20 houses. The results are shown in the table.
a Draw a bar chart to represent this information.
b Work out the total number of people living in the 20 houses.
c Find the mean number of people living per house.

Number of people	Number of houses in which that number of people were living
0	1
1	2
2	3
3	5
4	4
5	3
6	1
7	1

For Questions 11 to 20, give the answers to the nearest whole number.

11 ▦ The longest place name in the UK is that of a small station in Wales (coined by a local bard as a hoax!).

LLANFAIRPWLLGWYNGYLLGOGERYCHWYRNDROBWLLLLANTYSILIOGOGOGOCH

If the sign is 24 m long, find the mean number of letters per metre.

12 The main towers of the Humber suspension bridge are 155.5 m high. Each of them was constructed in 74 days. Find the mean height constructed per day.

13 The world mineshaft-sinking record was set in South Africa in 1962. In 31 days a shaft of 381.3 m was sunk. Find the mean depth sunk per day.

14 On a flight lasting 10 minutes, the wings of a fly vibrate 204 000 times. Find the mean number of times the wings vibrate per second.

15 The world air-speed record was set by a Lockheed SR-71A in 1976. It travelled 25 km in 25.5 seconds.
a Find the mean speed in km per hour.
b How far did it fly in one second?

16 This table shows the men's world record for seven distances on the track. Work out the mean speed, in metres per second, for each of the seven distances.

	Distance	Time
a	100 m	9.83 seconds
b	200 m	19.72 seconds
c	400 m	43.29 seconds
d	800 m	1 minute 41.73 seconds
e	1500 m	3 minutes 29.46 seconds
f	5000 m	12 minutes 58.39 seconds
g	10 000 m	27 minutes 13.81 seconds

17 On the Pacific island of Nauru, the population of 6100 drinks nearly 8 million litres of lager each year.
a Find the mean number of litres of lager drunk per person each year.
b Find the mean number of litres of lager drunk per day by each person.

18 **Investigate** the following figures:

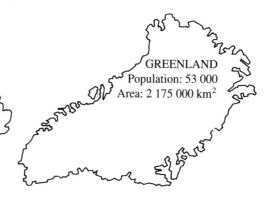

UNITED KINGDOM
Population: 54 398 000
Area: 229 988 km^2

GREENLAND
Population: 53 000
Area: 2 175 000 km^2

MONACO
Population: 27 000
Area: 1.914 km^2

MASTERMINDERS

19 In the UK approximately 80 000 tonnes of tobacco are smoked per year. Work out an estimate of the mean weight of tobacco smoked per person per day. (Take the population of the UK to be 54 million people.)

20 John cycles at 15 km/h for $2\frac{1}{2}$ hours and then at 17 km/h for 6 km. Find his mean speed.

Activity 19

For this Activity, each pupil in your class should be measured in height to the nearest centimetre.

1 Make a list of the results.

2 Find the mean height.

3 How many pupils are taller than the mean?

6.3 Probability

Probability is used to predict the likelihood of an event happening.

Activity 20

1 Throw an ordinary die 60 times and record the score for each throw.

2 Collect all the scores from the whole class in a table. Illustrate the results on a bar chart. Comment on the shape of the bar chart.

In this Activity you should have found that each score occurred about the same number of times. This is because each score is determined by chance and is equally likely to occur, that is, is equally 'probable'.

REMEMBER

An event which is determined by chance is called **random**.

___ *Activity 21*

A six-sided die was thrown 60 times and produced the scores shown below.

1, 3, 2, 4,   2, 4, 3, 1,   2, 6, 2, 1,   4, 6, 6, 2,   3, 2, 4, 1,

2, 3, 2, 6,   2, 6, 1, 2,   4, 2, 3, 4,   2, 4, 2, 6,   1, 3, 2, 2,

6, 1, 3, 2,   6, 4, 4, 2,   2, 3, 1, 2,   1, 2, 4, 6,   3, 1, 2, 2.

Investigate why this is called an unfair die.

___ **Exercise 37**

For each question, comment on the statement.

1   In the game of Snakes and Ladders, all players are equally likely to win.

2   In the game of Monopoly, each player has the same chance of winning.

3   From a shuffled pack of ordinary playing cards, I am just as likely to select a heart as a spade.

·4   Because the goal posts on a hockey pitch are the same size, both teams have the same chance of winning.

5   In a raffle, everyone who has bought a ticket is equally likely to win if the winning ticket is selected at random.

6   The teacher selects a pupil from a class at random. All pupils in the class have the same chance of being selected.

7   Two people cross a busy road. They are equally likely to be knocked down.

___ *Activity 22*

You will need a partner and one die between you.

1   Invent a **simple** game using one die, at which both of you have the same chance of winning.

2   Invent another **simple** game using one die where one of you has a better chance of winning than the other.

Play both games and comment on whether your rules worked.

___ *Activity 23*

You will need a partner for this Activity. Choose three playing cards each of a different value, for example, King, 10 and 6.

1 One pupil shuffles the three cards and places them face down on the table. The other pupil tries to guess which is the highest card. This is done 30 times by each pupil, and the results are collected using tally marks.

2 Copy the table and on it enter the results from the whole class.
From this experiment you should find that the highest card was picked correctly as a result of about one guess in three.

Outcome	Totals
Highest card picked	
Highest card not picked	

From this **experiment** we can say:

'The **expected probability** of picking the highest card is about one third.'

In **theory** (because we are picking one card out of three each time) we can say:

'The **theoretical probability** of picking the highest card is one third.'

> ___ *NOTE*
>
> The probability of an event happening $= \dfrac{\text{Number of desired outcomes}}{\text{Number of possible outcomes}}$

In Activity 23, the 'desired outcome' is picking the highest card, and the 'possible outcomes' are picking the highest card, picking the lowest card and picking the middle card.

■ *EXAMPLE 1*

A special die has its six faces marked Ace, Ace, Ace, King, King, Queen.
Find the probability of throwing **a** a King   **b** an Ace.

a [W]   Probability of a King

   [W] $= \dfrac{\text{Number of desired outcomes}}{\text{Number of possible outcomes}} = \dfrac{2}{6}$

   [A] $= \dfrac{1}{3}$

b [W]   Probability of an Ace

   [W] $= \dfrac{\text{Number of desired outcomes}}{\text{Number of possible outcomes}} = \dfrac{3}{6}$

   [A] $= \dfrac{1}{2}$

___ Exercise 38

1 A die has faces marked with the numbers 1, 2, 2, 3, 3, 3. Find the probability of throwing:
a 1 **b** 2 **c** 3

2 A die has faces marked with the numbers 4, 6, 6, 8, 8, 8. Find the probability of throwing:
a 4 **b** 6 **c** 8

3 A die has faces marked with the numbers 1, 2, 3, 5, 8, 13. Find the probability of throwing:
a an odd number **b** an even number. Comment on your answers.

4 An ordinary die is thrown. Find the probability of throwing:
a a number greater than 6 **b** a number less than 7. Comment on your answers.

5 A thousand raffle tickets are sold. Mrs Jones buys 25 of them. What is the probability of her winning first prize?

6 A roulette wheel has the numbers 0 to 36 on it.
What is the probability of obtaining:
a The number 27?
b An even number?
c A number less than 6?

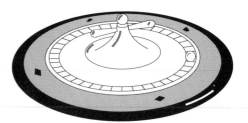

7 Six cards were selected at random from an ordinary pack of cards. These six cards were shuffled and from them one card was selected at random and its value noted. This was done 60 times. The results were:

K, 6, 4, 6, A, 5, 4, A, 6, 5,
4, A, 6, 4, K, 5, 4, 6, A, K,
A, 4, 6, A, A, K, 6, 4, A, 4,
6, 4, K, 4, 5, 6, 4, K, 4, A,
5, 6, K, 4, 4, 4, 5, A, 6, 4,
A, 4, 5, A, 6, 5, 4, A, K, A.

a Using tally marks, put this information into a table.
b Represent the information on a bar chart.
c Name the six cards.
d What was the probability of selecting (i) 6 (ii) 5 (iii) 4?

MASTERMINDER

8 Two ordinary dice are thrown at the same time. Work out the probability of throwing **a** a double **b** a total score of 7.
Justify your answers by experiment.

___ Revision Exercise 6A

Calculators are **not allowed**.

1 A survey is carried out to find the number of people in each of 50 cars passing a certain point.
   The results are:
   1, 2, 1, 3, 4, 1, 1, 2, 2, 1, 4, 1, 2, 4, 1, 2, 1, 1, 3, 3, 1, 2, 1, 1, 1,
   1, 2, 3, 2, 3, 2, 1, 1, 1, 3, 4, 3, 1, 2, 1, 3, 1, 2, 3, 4, 1, 2, 1, 3, 4.
   a Tabulate these results.   **b** Draw a suitable bar chart.
   c What fraction of the total number of cars had fewer than three people in them?
   d Work out the mean number of people per car.

2 An ordinary die is thrown. What is the probability of throwing a 6?

3 A die has faces marked with the numbers 2, 4, 4, 6, 6, 6. Find the probability of throwing:
   a a 2   **b** a 4   **c** a 6   **d** an even number.

4 The diagram shows Aaron's counter on
   part of a Snakes and Ladders board.
   On his next throw, with an ordinary die,
   what is the probability that Aaron will:
   a go 'down' a snake   **b** go 'up' a ladder
   c go neither 'up' nor 'down'?

5 An InterCity train leaves Peterborough at 17:36 and arrives in London at 18:28. If the distance
   is 104 miles, find the mean speed of the journey in miles per hour.

___ Revision Exercise 6B

Calculators are **not allowed**.

1 The table shows the number of goals scored by
   a school hockey team in 20 matches.
   a Draw a bar chart to represent this information.
   b Copy and complete: 'More than 2 goals were
      scored in ...% of the matches'.
   c Find the mean number of goals scored per
      match.

Number of goals	Number of matches in which they scored that number of goals
0	2
1	6
2	7
3	3
4	2

2 Find the mean of the following ages:
   9 years 4 months,   10 years 5 months,   10 years 10 months,   11 years 2 months,
   9 years 11 months.

3 An ordinary die is thrown. Find the probability of throwing a number: **a** greater than 3   **b** 3
   c less than 3. Comment on your answers.

4 A card is selected at random from an ordinary pack of 52 playing cards. Find the probability
   that it is: **a** a heart   **b** a black card   **c** an Ace   **d** a Joker

5 You spin a coin. I spin a coin.
   a List the four possible outcomes.
   b What is the probability that we both spin: (i) tails   (ii) a different result from each other?

— Basics Test 6

A Calculator

    1 Solve for a: $28 + a = 36.7$ **2** Solve for b: $24 = b - 4.083$

    3 Solve for c: $\frac{c}{62} = 38$ **4** Solve for d: $17d = 544$

    5 $0.096 \times 0.0015 \times 450$ **6** Express £9.72 as a percentage of £21.60.

B Paper and pencil

    7 Solve for e: $\frac{4032}{e} = 36$ **8** Solve for f: $32.4 - f = 29.85$

    9 $35 \times 18 \div 42$ **10** 3.84×0.015

    11 £1.37−£3.58   **12** Reduce $\frac{75}{90}$ to its lowest terms.

    13 Simplify $b + b + b + c$.   **14** Change $\frac{16}{25}$ to a percentage.

    15 Work out an approximation to $(0.7123)^2$.

C Mental

    Ten questions will be read out to you. Use the following facts to answer Questions 16 to 20:
    $a = 3,$ $b = 6,$ $c = 18.$

— Puzzlers

The following question is taken from Thomas Thomas's Mathematics textbook written in 1791.

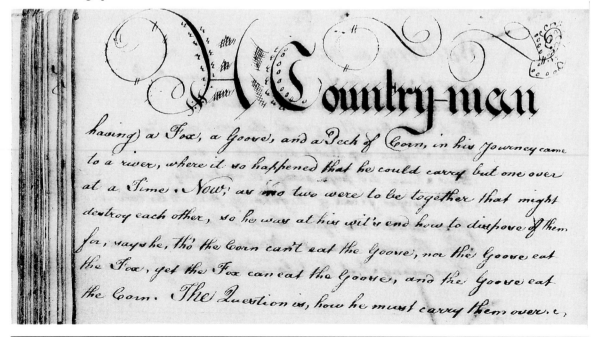

Coursework: Form-marks investigation

Your teacher will read out a set of marks for your class. How pleased or disappointed should you be? This Coursework will try to answer this question.

(Whenever you write down facts or figures about your own mark and position, write them in red. You will need a calculator.)

1 Write down the full details of everyone in your class on a table like the one below.

Class:	Date:	Maximum marks:	
Name		Mark	Position

2 Copy and complete the following table, writing each percentage to the nearest whole number.

Position in class	1st	2nd	3rd	4th etc.
Mark				
Percentage				

a Write down the names of those who came in (i) the top half   (ii) the top quarter (iii) the bottom quarter.

b Work out the mean mark per pupil. Write down the names of those who obtained more than the mean mark. Compare your list of names with those in part 2a (i). Try to explain any differences.

3 Copy and complete the table below.

Marks (%) in the	10's	20's	30's	40's	50's	60's	70's	80's	90's
Number of pupils									

a Draw a bar chart to illustrate these figures.

b Comment on (i) the shape of your bar chart, (ii) its position on the horizontal axis, (iii) whether you think your teacher is pleased with the overall results.

EXTENSION

4 A pupil is selected **at random** from the class.

a If the pass mark were 45%, what would be the probability of selecting a pupil who had failed?

b If 15% of your class had failed, estimate the probability of selecting a pupil who had passed.

7 GEOMETRY I

— 7.1 Basic principles

— Grid references

Maps which have a grid superimposed on them allow regions and places to be easily identified. A six-figure grid reference denotes a point (see Chapter 2).

A four-figure grid reference denotes a grid square. On this map-grid the shaded region is denoted by the four-figure grid reference (2645).

The five points are denoted by the following six-figure grid references:

A (260435)   B (255445)   C (270440)
D (264448)   E (277443)

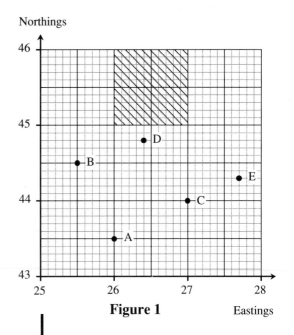

Figure 1   Eastings

 REMEMBER

Grid references: Eastings before Northings

— Co-ordinates

With x and y axes, points are denoted by 'co-ordinates' and written (x, y).

The six points are denoted as follows:

A (2, 3)   B (1, −2)
C (−1, 3)   D (−2, −3)
E (−2, 0)   F (0, −1)

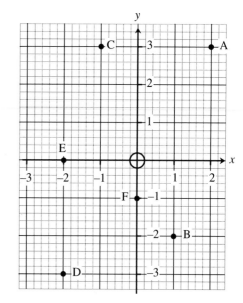

Figure 2

 REMEMBER

Co-ordinates: (x, y)

108

—— Exercise 39

1   Make a map-grid like that in Figure 1, and shade the regions 2544 and 2743.
Plot the points P (265440), Q (275451), R (271459), S (253458).

2   Copy the x and y axes shown in Figure 2. On your axes plot the points: G (2, 1), H (1, −3),
I (3, −1), J (−1, 2), K (−2, 1), L (−1, −1), M (−2, −2), N (−3, −3), O (3, −3)

—— 7.2 Measuring angles

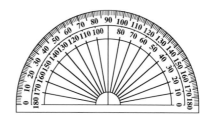

Angles are measured in degrees (°)
by using a protractor.

We will denote angles in three
ways as shown here, where angle
$a = A\hat{B}C = \hat{B} = 40°$. (Other books
may also use $\angle ABC$.)

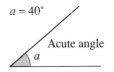

$a = 40°$

Acute angle
a

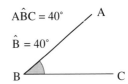

$A\hat{B}C = 40°$ A

$\hat{B} = 40°$

B ———— C

Angles between 0° and 90° are
known as 'acute angles', whereas
angles between 90° and 180° are
known as 'obtuse angles'.

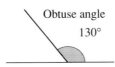

Obtuse angle
130°

A 'right angle' is an angle of 90°.
This is an important case.

90°

A straight line is an angle of 180°.
This is also an important case.

180°

In order to turn around and face in the opposite direction you must turn yourself through
an angle of 180°.

In order to turn yourself right around and face the same way again you must turn through
an angle of 360°.

A 'reflex angle' is an angle between
180° and 360°. Reflex angles
cannot be measured directly with a
semicircular protractor. Examples
of reflex angles, angles of 240° and
310°, are illustrated here.

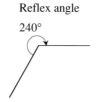

Reflex angle
240°

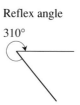

Reflex angle
310°

■ *EXAMPLE 1*

Use a protractor to measure each of the following: **a** angle x **b** $\hat{Z}$ **c** $Z\hat{Q}P$ **d** reflex angle $X\hat{Y}Z$

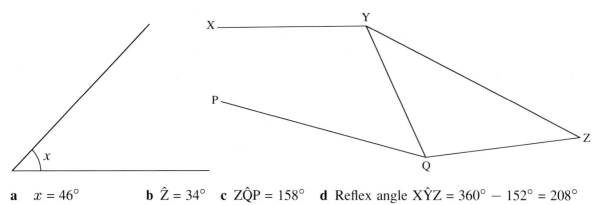

a $x = 46°$ **b** $\hat{Z} = 34°$ **c** $Z\hat{Q}P = 158°$ **d** Reflex angle $X\hat{Y}Z = 360° - 152° = 208°$

___ *Activity 24*

On this diagram estimate the size of each of the marked angles, then use your protractor to measure each angle. Tabulate your results and keep them for Activity 27 on page 116.

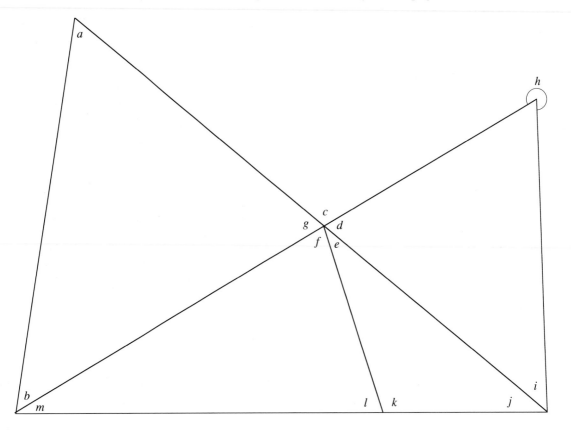

__ *Activity 25*

In this Activity you are going to measure each angle inside four different shapes. However, **before you measure** the angles, write down an estimate of each.

Draw up a table with these headings and use it to enter your results.

Part	Angle	Estimate	Measurement	Difference*	Angle total
1	XYZ				

* This is the difference between your estimate and the measurement.

1 Draw any large triangle and label the corners X, Y and Z. Measure the angles XYZ, YZX and ZXY and enter the results in the table.

2 Measure the angles ABC, BCD, CDA and DAB in Figure 1 and enter the results in your table. Write down the co-ordinates of A, B, C and D.

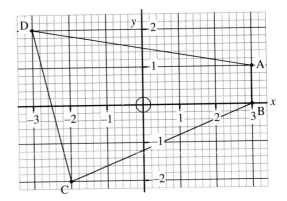

Figure 1

3 The map-grid in Figure 2 shows the course for a speed-boat race.

Measure the angles *a*, *b*, *c*, *d* and *e* and enter the results in your table. Write down the grid reference of each of the five points.

4 On a piece of A5 graph paper, draw a *y* axis from 8 to −8 using a scale of 1 cm to 1 unit and draw an *x* axis from 6 to −6 using the same scale.

Plot the figure ABCDEF where the co-ordinates of each corner are:
A (6, 4), B (2, 7),
C (−5, 4), D (−4, −4),
E (1, −7), F (5, −6).

Measure the angles ABC, BCD, CDE, DEF, EFA and FAB and enter the results in your table.

For each of the four shapes work out, to the nearest 10°, the total of all the measured angles, and enter it in your table. Comment on your results.

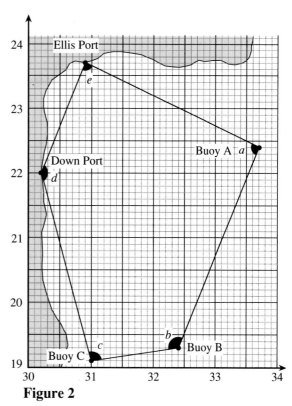

Figure 2

_ 7.3 Line symmetry of triangles

_ Activity 26

1 **a** Fold a piece of paper in half. With
a pair of scissors, cut into the fold to
make a symmetrical shape such as the
one shown here.

b Explain why:
(i) The fold is sometimes called
either the 'mirror line' or the 'line
of symmetry'.
(ii) The shape and size of the area on
each side of the fold is the same.

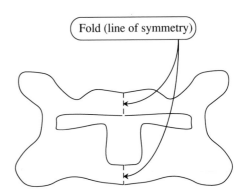

Fold (line of symmetry)

NOTE

Regions which have the same size and shape are called **congruent**.

---

2 From another piece of folded paper, and by making **only two cuts into the fold**, try to cut out
four different types of triangle:
a One angle less than 90°. **b** All angles equal to 60°.
c One angle equal to 90°. **d** One angle more than 90°.

In the triangle with equal angles, make two more folds to find two other lines of symmetry.
Stick each of the four triangles into your book by putting glue only on the shaded part shown
below. Label each with its correct name. Now fold each triangle along the lines of symmetry
to investigate the pairs of equal angles and sides.

a Isosceles
acute-angled

b Equilateral

c Isosceles
right-angled

d Isosceles
obtuse-angled

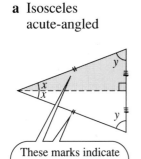

These marks indicate
equal lengths.

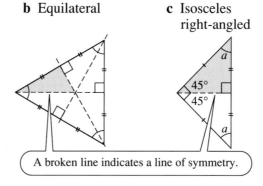

A broken line indicates a line of symmetry.

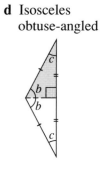

The importance of these facts about isosceles and equilateral triangles is that if one is true all the others are true. This helps us to deduce facts about these two types of triangle. Look carefully at Examples 1 and 2 below.

(Triangles with no line of symmetry are called scalene. These can be right angled, acute angled or obtuse angled.)

> **REMEMBER**
>
> **Isosceles triangles**
> - 1 line of symmetry
> - 2 equal angles
> - 2 equal sides
>
> **Equilateral triangles**
> - 3 lines of symmetry
> - 3 equal angles
> - 3 equal sides

■ EXAMPLE 1

Given that LO is the line of symmetry of triangle LMN, write down all the properties of the triangle.

Triangle LMN is isosceles.
LM = LN and LÑO = LM̂O
LÔN = 90° = LÔM
ML̂O = NL̂O
Triangles LOM and LON are congruent.

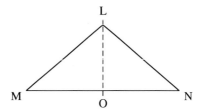

■ EXAMPLE 2

Given that triangle WXZ is isosceles, copy and complete the following statements and give the reason for each in the brackets.

a WX = ...(......)
b XŴY = ...(......)

a WX = WZ (Triangle WXZ is isosceles)
b XŴY = ZŴY (Triangle WXZ is isosceles)

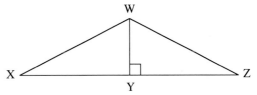

⎯ Exercise 40

For Questions 1 to 6 draw axes for x and y from 4 to −4, using the same scale on both axes.

1 Plot points A(3, 3), B(−3, 1), C(3, −1). Join them to make a triangle.
 a What sort of triangle is ABC?
 b Which sides are equal in length?

2 Plot points X(1, 4), Y(4, −1), Z(−2, −1). Join them to make a triangle.
 a What sort of triangle is XYZ?
 b Name two equal angles.

3 Plot points M(4, 3), N(1, −2), L(−2, 3), O(1, 3). Join LM, MN and NL to make a triangle. Join ON.
 a Name two triangles which are congruent.
 b What sort of triangle is OMN?

4 Plot points A(2, 3), B(4, −2), C(−3, 1), D(−1, −4). Join AB, BC and CA to make a triangle. Join AD to make the line of symmetry.

    a What sort of triangle is ABC?   **b** Name three angles equal to DÂB.

5 Draw two triangles, not touching, which are congruent. Write down the co-ordinates of the six corners.

6 Is it possible to draw an equilateral triangle so that x and y, in the co-ordinates (x, y), are whole numbers for all three corners?

For Questions 7 to 27, copy and complete the given statement and give reasons in the brackets. (△ means triangle.)

7 In △ ABC, AB̂C = AĈB:

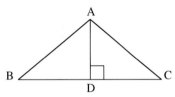

    a AB = AC (......)
    b BD = DC (......)

8

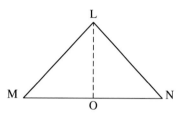

    a MO = ... (......)
    b LM̂O = ... (......)

9

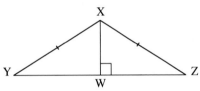

    a WX is the line of symmetry (......)
    b △ XYW is congruent to △ ... (......)

10

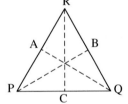

    a PQ̂R = ...° (......)
    b PQ̂A = ...° (......)

11 Given that △ PRS and △ PQS are congruent:

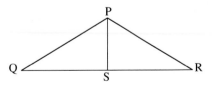

    a PQ = ... (......)
    b PQ̂S = ... (......)
    c △ PRQ is ... (......)

12

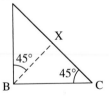

    a BÂX = ...° (......)
    b AX = BX (......)
    c △ BXC is ... (......)

13 a DB is the ... (......)
    b AB = ... (......)
    c DB̂C = ...° (......)

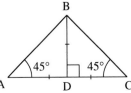

Questions 14 to 27 all refer to the diagram on the right.

14 △AGC is isosceles (. . . . . .)

15 BÂG = 30° (. . . . . .)

16 AĜB = CĜB (. . . . . .)

17 △FCG is ... (. . . . . .)

18 GF̂C = ...° (. . . . . .)

19 △... has 3 axes of symmetry (. . . . . .)

20 △FDE is ... (. . . . . .)

21 FE = FD (. . . . . .)

22 △FDC is ... (. . . . . .)

23 FD̂C = ...° (. . . . . .)

24 AĈF = ...° (. . . . . .)

25 AĈD = ...° (. . . . . .)

26 CD̂E = ...° (. . . . . .)

27 EÂC + AĈD + CD̂E + DÊA = ...°

MASTERMINDER

28 In the diagram below, BÔF = CÔG = 90°.
a Explain why
(i) triangle OEC is equilateral
(ii) EF = BC.
b Write down the size of
(i) OÊD   (ii) GD̂O   (iii) AÔB   (iv) AÔG
(v) BÔC   (vi) OB̂C   (vii) AÔE   (viii) AÔF.
c Explain why OE = AC.

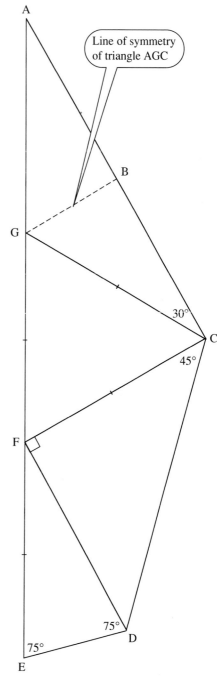

This diagram is not
drawn accurately.

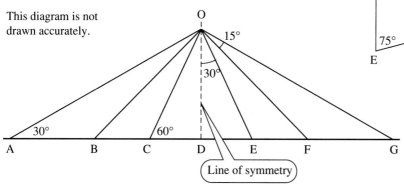

___ 7.4 Angle properties

___ *Activity 27*

Using your measured angles from Activity 24, page 110, copy and complete the following table.

Angles	Angle total	Comment
a, b, g		
f, m, l		
k, e, j		
c, d		
c, g		
g, f, e		
f, e, d		
c, d, e, f, g		

What do you notice about the following angles:
a *g* and *d* **b** *c* and (*f* + *e*)?

If your measurements were reasonably accurate, you will have demonstrated four very important rules of geometry:

> ___ *REMEMBER*
>
> - The angle sum of a triangle is 180°.
> - The angles on a straight line total 180°.
> - The sum of the angles at a point is 360°.
> - Vertically opposite angles are equal.

■*EXAMPLE 1*

Find the unknown angle, giving the reason.

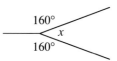

  [F]   See diagram.

  [E], [S]   160° + 160° + *x* = 360°   (Angles at a point)

  [W]   320° + *x* = 360°

                  x = 360° − 320° = 40°

■ EXAMPLE 2

Find each of the following, giving reasons.
a   The value of m.
b   The size of WÔY.
c   The size of VÔY.

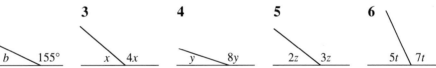

a   [F]   See diagram.

   [E], [S] $m + 2m = 180°$ (Angles on a straight line)

   [W] $3m = 180°$

                 $m = \dfrac{180°}{3}$

                 $m = 60°$

b   WÔY = 60° (Vertically opposite)
c   VÔY = 120° (Vertically opposite or angles on a straight line)

____ Exercise 41

For Questions 1 to 6, find the unknown angles, giving reasons.

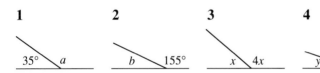

1	2	3	4	5	6
35° a	b 155°	x 4x	y 8y	2z 3z	5t 7t

7 Find:
a The value of u.
b The size of BÔD.
c The size of BÔC.

8 Find:
a The value of t.
b The size of MÔP.
c The size of NÔP.

9 Find:
a The value of n.
b The size of XÔY.
c The size of WÔY.

10 Find:
a The value of m.
b The size of RÔT.
c The size of SÔT.

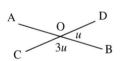
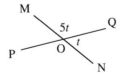
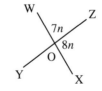

For Questions 11 to 16, find the unknown angles.

11	12	13	14	15	16

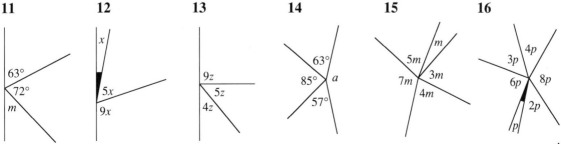

MASTERMINDERS

For Questions 17 to 22, find the unknown angles.

17 $b = 2a$
$c = 3b$

18 $y = 5x$
$z = 6y$

19 $b = \dfrac{1}{2}a$
$c = 3b$
$d = 2c$

20 $n = \dfrac{1}{3}m$
$p = 4n$
$q = 4p$

21 $u = t + 15°$
$v = u + 15°$

22 $q = p + 20°$
$r = q + 20°$

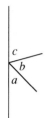 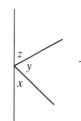 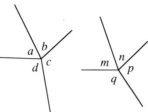 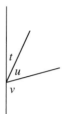 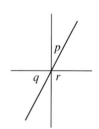

___ 7.5 Angles of a triangle

■*EXAMPLE 1*
Find the unknown angles, giving reasons.

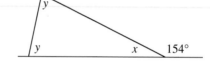

[F]   See diagram.

[E], [S] $154° + x = 180°$ (Angles on straight line)

[W] $x = 180° - 154°$

        $x = 26°$

[E], [S] $26° + y + y = 180°$ (Angle sum of triangle)

[W] $2y = 180° - 26°$

        $y = \dfrac{154°}{2}$

        $y = 77°$

___ Exercise 42

For Questions 1 to 4, find the unknown angles, giving reasons.

1

2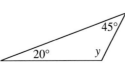

3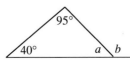

4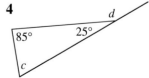

For Questions 5 to 14, find the unknown angles, giving reasons.

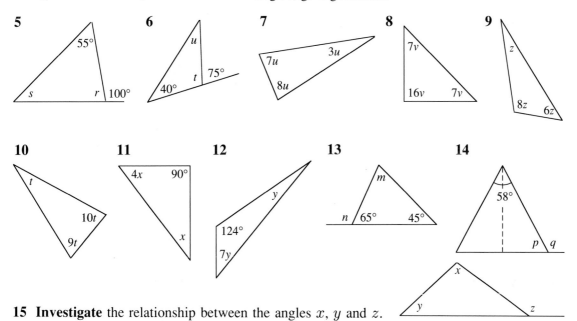

15 Investigate the relationship between the angles x, y and z.

16 Investigate the following statement: 'In any triangle, the longest side is always opposite the largest angle'.

MASTERMINDERS

For Questions 17 to 20, find the unknown angles.

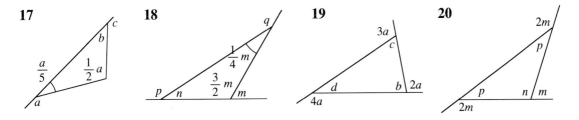

21 Work out the sum of all the marked angles.

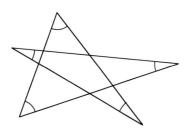

___ *Activity 28*

The diagram shows a Ferris Wheel of the type used at a funfair. There are as many chairs as spokes and the chairs are equally spaced around the wheel.

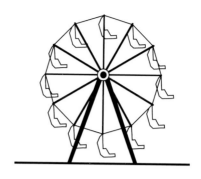

1 This diagram represents a Ferris Wheel with six spokes.
Work out the value of **a** x **b** y **c** $12y$.

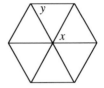

2 The results of part 1 are shown on the table below, where n is the number of spokes. Copy and complete it.

n	x	y	$2n$	$2ny$
6	60°	60°	12	720°
4				
8				
18				
36				
360				

a Explain the significance of the numbers in the last column.
b If $2ny = 3240°$, how many chairs would you expect on the Ferris Wheel?

___ **7.6** Regular polygons

'Polygon' is the name given to a shape with any number of sides.

___ *Activity 29*

ABCDE is a regular pentagon drawn inside a circle with centre marked O.

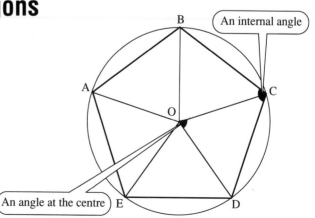

An internal angle

An angle at the centre

1 Measure the size of each of the 15 angles and the length of each of the 10 lines. List your measurements. What do you notice?
   a Why are the five angles at the centre each 72°?
   b Why is AO = BO = CO = DO = EO?
   c Why are the five triangles congruent?
   d Why is ABCDE a **regular** pentagon?

2 Construct a regular pentagon by following these stages:
   a Work out the angle at the centre.

     [W]   Angle at centre

     [W] $= \dfrac{360°}{5}$ _Divide by 5 because it is a regular pentagon_

     [A] $= 72°$

   b Draw five angles of 72° around a point O.

   c Put your compass point on O and draw a circle.

   d Join up the points on the circle to make a regular pentagon. Measure each of the sides and comment on the result.

3 Construct a regular octagon (8-sided figure) inside a circle of radius 5 cm.

REMEMBER

Shapes which are **regular** have equal sides and equal internal angles.

Revision Exercise 7A

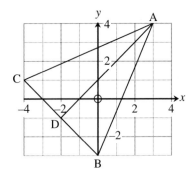

1 **a** What are the co-ordinates of A?
   b Measure AB, AC, AB̂C, AĈB and the
       reflex angle CÂB.
   c What sort of triangle is ABC?
   d Copy and complete:
       (i) AD is the ... triangle ABC.
       (ii) Triangles ACD and ABD are ...

2 (A broken line indicates a line of symmetry.)
   Copy and complete:
   a AB̂C = ...°   **b** BÂF = ...°
   c AF̂C = ...°   **d** BD̂C = ...°

3 Find the lettered angles:

a   **b** 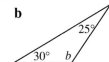   **c**   **d**

4 Make a neat drawing of a regular five-sided figure of any size.

Revision Exercise 7B

1 In this figure, triangles AZY and AZX are congruent.
   Copy and complete:
   a Triangle XYZ is ...
   b ZA is the ... triangle XYZ.
   c ZX̂A = ...°   **d** ZÂY = ...°

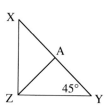

2 Find the lettered angles.

a   **b**   **c**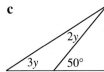

3 Make a neat drawing, of any size, of a
   regular 10-sided figure. On your drawing
   write down the size of each of the angles
   in the figure.

4 PQ (see diagram) is one side of an
   isosceles triangle PQR where R has whole
   number co-ordinates. How many positions
   for R can you find?

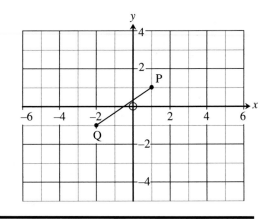

Basics Test 7

A Calculator

   1 $13.72 - 2.49 - 26.98$ **2** $105 \times 1.26 \div 0.45$

   3 Solve for a: $\frac{a}{21} = 34$ **4** Solve for b: $58b = 522$

   5 Solve for c: $78 = \frac{624}{c}$

   6 Find the mean, to the nearest tenth, of: 4.8, 6.4, 3.9, 5.3, 4.1, 7.2

B Paper and pencil

   7 Solve for d: $0.655 + d = 5.34$ **8** Solve for e: $4.8 = e - 3.9$

   9 Solve for f: $7.1 - f = 5.7$ **10** When $a = 3$, what is $2a + 6a$?

   11 Change 543.2 cm to metres.   **12** What is $\frac{2}{5}$ of 1 hour in minutes?

   13 $\frac{1.6 \times 0.75}{3}$ **14** $\frac{1}{6} + \frac{5}{12} + \frac{3}{4}$

   15 Work out an approximation to 3789.23×0.2893

C Mental

   Ten questions will be read out to you. Use the following facts to answer Questions 16 to 20:

   $a = 3, \quad b = 5, \quad c = 21$

Puzzlers

1 A kangaroo chases a rabbit. The kangaroo takes two jumps while the rabbit takes three jumps, but each jump that the kangaroo takes covers as much distance as two of the rabbit's jumps. If, at the beginning of the chase, the rabbit is ten jumps ahead of the kangaroo, how many jumps will the rabbit take before the kangaroo catches him?

2 Each of the fractions $\frac{1}{2}, \frac{1}{3}, \frac{1}{4}, \frac{1}{5}, \frac{1}{6}, \frac{1}{7}, \frac{1}{8}, \frac{1}{9}$ can be written by using all the digits from 1 to 9 inclusive. Look at the two examples below:

$$\frac{1}{2} = \frac{6729}{13458} \qquad \frac{1}{3} = \frac{5832}{17496}$$

Copy the following and fill in the blank spaces:

$$\frac{1}{4} = \frac{4\ 3\ 9\ \bigcirc}{\bigcirc\ 7\ 5\ 6\ 8} \qquad \frac{1}{5} = \frac{2\ 7\ 6\ 9}{1\ 3\ \bigcirc\ 4\ \bigcirc} \qquad \frac{1}{6} = \frac{\bigcirc\bigcirc\bigcirc\bigcirc}{1\ 7\ 6\ 5\ 8}$$

$$\frac{1}{7} = \frac{2\ 3\ 9\ 4}{\bigcirc\bigcirc\bigcirc\bigcirc\bigcirc} \qquad \frac{1}{8} = \frac{3\ \bigcirc\ 8\ 7}{\bigcirc\bigcirc\bigcirc\bigcirc\bigcirc} \qquad \frac{1}{9} = \frac{6\ \bigcirc\bigcirc\bigcirc}{\bigcirc\ 7\ \bigcirc\bigcirc\ 9}$$

What do you notice about $\frac{1}{4}, \frac{1}{6}$ and $\frac{1}{7}$?

Coursework: Polygons

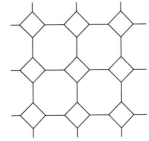

Figure 1

(Before starting this Coursework make sure that you have done Activity 29 on page 120.)

Certain regular shapes fit together as shown in Figure 1. Mathematical shapes have fascinated people through the ages. The Greek mathematician Pappus, who lived in the fourth century AD, said that 'God has given even the unreasoning creatures a partial share of mathematics'. Could he have been thinking of the honey bee?

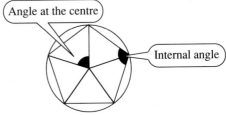

Figure 2

1 Draw each of the eight regular polygons shown in the table below, inside circles of radius 3 cm. Measure the length of one side and one internal angle (see Figure 2).

Copy and complete the table.

Number of sides	Name of figure	Angle at the centre	Internal angle	Side length (cm)
3				
4				
5				
6				
7				
8				
10				
12				

2 With a compass point, mark through onto a piece of card each of the eight regular polygons you have drawn. Carefully cut out each shape.

a Use your cut-outs to find which regular polygons, with the same number of sides, could fit exactly around a point with no gaps.

b Describe briefly why you think the honey bee should have chosen to make its honeycomb out of regular hexagons.

EXTENSION

3 a Figure 1 is made from two different regular polygons, each of the same side length, which fit together with no gaps. How many other similar patterns can you make? Draw separate diagrams to illustrate each pattern.

b **Investigate** the sequences of numbers in the last three columns of the table.

8 ALGEBRA II

8.1 Basic principles

Simplifying

Remember you can only add or subtract things of the same type. For example,

    1 book + 1 book + 1 book = 3 books

and   £3 + £2 − £1 = £4

and   1 pen + 2 pens + 1 rat = 3 pens + 1 rat

When simplifying terms in algebra the same rule applies. For example,

    $1b + 1b + 1b = 3b$

(This could have been written without the number 1 in front of each 'b', that is $b + b + b = 3b$.)

and $p + 2p + r = 3p + r$

> *REMEMBER*
>
> - Adding and subtracting: **'like terms' only**
> - $y + y + y + y + y + y + y$ means 7 lots of y
>   or $7 \times y = 7y$

Equations

In this chapter you will learn how equations can be used to solve problems.

> *REMEMBER*
>
> There is only **one rule** to solving equations:
> you must do the **same operation to both sides**.

If this is done, the balance of the equation is not changed. Look carefully at Example 1 on the next page, which illustrates the principle using a simple weighing balance.

■ *EXAMPLE 1*

a Solve the equation $4x = 12$.

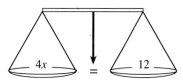

Divide both sides by 4.

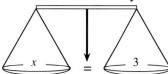

c Solve the equation $x - 4 = 7$.

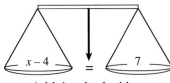

Add 4 to both sides.

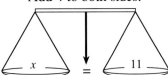

b Solve the equation $x + 2 = 10$.

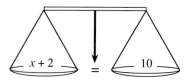

Subtract 2 from both sides.

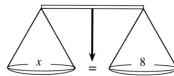

d Solve the equation $\dfrac{x}{5} = 9$.

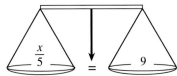

Multiply both sides by 5.

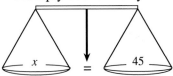

The following two equations are of a slightly different type and in each case the x has to be moved first. However, the same rule applies.

e Solve the equation $\dfrac{5}{x} = 4$.

$$\frac{5}{x} = 4 \quad \text{(Multiply both sides by } x\text{)}$$

$$5 = 4x \quad \text{(Divide both sides by 4)}$$

$$\frac{5}{4} = x$$

$$x = 1\tfrac{1}{4}$$

f Solve the equation $3 - x = 15$.

$$3 - x = 15 \quad \text{(Add } x \text{ to both sides)}$$

$$3 = 15 + x \quad \text{(Subtract 15 from both sides)}$$

$$3 - 15 = x$$

$$x = -12$$

▬ Substitution

When using equations to solve problems, the **facts** of the problem must first be substituted into the equation.

┌─ *REMEMBER*

1 Write down the **facts**.   [F]

2 Write down the **equation**.   [E]

3 **Substitute** the facts.   [S]

4 Finally do the **working**.   [W]

■ *EXAMPLE 2*

When $k = 6$ and $p = 1.2$, find the value of t in **a** $k = t + p$ **b** $\frac{t}{k} = p$ **c** $\frac{p}{t} = k$

a [F] $k = 6, \quad p = 1.2$

[E] $k = t + p$

[S] $6 = t + 1.2$ (Subtract 1.2 from both sides)

[W] $6 - 1.2 = t$

$t = 4.8$

b [F] $k = 6, \quad p = 1.2$

[E] $\dfrac{t}{k} = p$

[S] $\dfrac{t}{6} = 1.2$ (Multiply both sides by 6)

[W] $t = 1.2 \times 6$

$t = 7.2$

c [F] $k = 6, \quad p = 1.2$

[E] $\dfrac{p}{t} = k$

[S] $\dfrac{1.2}{t} = 6$ (Multiply both sides by t)

[W] $1.2 = 6t$ (Divide both sides by 6)

$\dfrac{1.2}{6} = t$

$t = 0.2$

___ Exercise 43

1 Simplify:

   a $3a + 2a$ **b** $14b - 6b$ **c** $4q + q$ **d** $19x - 18x$

2 Simplify:

   a $2a + 3a + 4a$ **b** $9p - 7p + 2p$ **c** $14c + 6c - 7c$ **d** $32x - 30x - x$

3 Simplify:

   a $d + d + d + d$ **b** $e + e + e - e$ **c** $f + f - f + f$ **d** $g - g - g - g$

4 Simplify:

   a $5x + 6x - 2y$ **b** $8a - a + 3b$ **c** $6z + 5v - 2z$ **d** $7r - 6t - 4r$

5 Solve for x:

   a $3x = 27$ **b** $x - 24 = 6$ **c** $\frac{x}{3} = 27$ **d** $\frac{24}{x} = 6$

6 Solve for v:

   a $v + 2 = 5$ **b** $13 = 6v$ **c** $31 = \frac{v}{4}$ **d** $6 = \frac{13}{v}$

7 Solve for b:

   a $28 = b + 30$ **b** $16 = b - 32$ **c** $28 = 30 - b$ **d** $\frac{16}{b} = 32$

8 Solve for c:

   a $3c = 10$ **b** $2.25 = \frac{c}{4}$ **c** $\frac{22}{c} = 4$ **d** $13 = 4 - c$

9 Simplify:

   a $2.3x + 9.2x$ **b** $1.9y - 1.3y$ **c** $5.6a + a + 4.9a$ **d** $4.9a - 5.2a$

10 Simplify:

   a $b + 2.3r + 2r$ **b** $t + 4.3s - 7.8s$ **c** $4y - 5x - 5y$ **d** $x - 2y - 6x$

For Questions 11 to 15, find which, of **a**, **b** and **c**, has a different answer from the other two.

11 ▦ **a** $y + 32 = 80$ **b** $3y = 126$ **c** $\frac{y}{3} = 14$

12 ▦ **a** $6.5 + u = 30.5$ **b** $2.5u = 75$ **c** $\frac{u}{8} = 3.75$

13 ▦ **a** $n - 1.45 = 2.75$ **b** $1.2n = 5.4$ **c** $\frac{n}{12} = 0.35$

14 ▦ **a** $10.25 - y = 2.75$ **b** $1.25y = 10$ **c** $\frac{y}{20} = 0.4$

15 ▦ **a** $0.02y = 0.5$ **b** $\frac{y}{32} = 0.75$ **c** $\frac{60}{y} = 2.5$

MASTERMINDERS

For Questions 16 to 18, $a = 2$, $b = 4$ and $c = 5$.

16 Solve for x: **a** $\frac{1}{2}ab = 6c - x$ **b** $c = \frac{4}{-x}$

17 When $4ax = 5b$ and $y + c = ab$, find the value of xy.

18 When $\frac{2b}{m} = 3c$ and $n - \frac{3}{b} = \frac{3}{a}$, find the value of mn.

— 8.2 Area

Area is a measure of how large a surface is. Area is measured in square units, the most common being square millimetres (mm^2), square centimetres (cm^2) and square metres (m^2).

— Rectangles

The area of a rectangle is found by multiplying the length by the breadth.

> ┌— **REMEMBER**
>
> Area (A) of rectangle = Length (l) × Breadth (b)

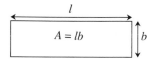

■ *EXAMPLE 1*

A rectangular field has an area of $2460\,m^2$. If its length is 82 m, find its breadth.

[F]   See diagram.

[E] $A = lb$

[S] $2460 = 82b$ (Divide both sides by 82)

[W] $\dfrac{2460}{82} = b$

         $b = 30\,m$ (Don't forget to include the units.)

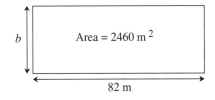

■ *EXAMPLE 2*

A rectangular garden is 45 m long and 25 m wide. It has a rectangular pond in it which measures 5 m by 4.5 m. Work out the area of garden which is **not** taken up by the pond.

[F]   See diagram.

[E]   Area of garden not pond = Area of garden − Area of pond

[S] $= (25 \times 45) - (5 \times 4.5)\,m^2$

[W] $= 1125 - 22.5\,m^2$

     $= 1102.5\,m^2$

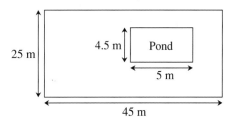

129

— Exercise 44

1 A rectangle has an area of 48 cm². Find its breadth if its length is:
    a 16 cm   **b** 20 cm   **c** 30 cm

2 A rectangle has an area of 600 mm². Find its length if its breadth is:
    a 24 mm   **b** 15 mm   **c** 20 mm

3 ▦ A rectangle has an area of 78 cm². Find its length if its breadth is:
    a 6.5 cm   **b** 1.3 cm   **c** 4.875 cm

4 ▦ A rectangle has an area of 100 m². Find, to the nearest metre, its length if its breadth is:
    a 7 m   **b** 5.7 m   **c** 9.3 m

5 ▦ A rectangular path has an area of 2.7 m² and is 4.5 m long. Find its width in centimetres.

6 A rectangular garden is 24 m wide and 35 m long. It has a rectangular flower bed in it which is 3 m long and 2.5 m wide. Find the area of garden which is not taken up by the flower bed.

7 The diagram shows a rectangular garden with a rockery in it. The rockery covers an area of 14.6 m². What is the area of garden not covered by the rockery?

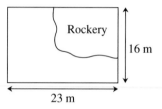

8 The diagram shows a rectangular pond 7 m long and 3 m wide with a path around it of width 1 m. Find:
    a The total area of the pond and the path.
    b The area of the path.

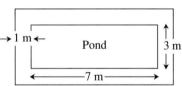

9 ▦ A picture frame has the dimensions shown here.
Find the area of the frame.

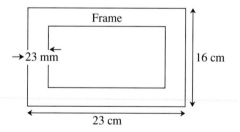

10 ▦ The diagram represents a path, 2 m wide, which has been laid part way around a house. The path is to be covered with square paving slabs of side length 50 cm.
    a Find the area of the path.
    b Find the total cost of paving slabs if each one costs £5.50.

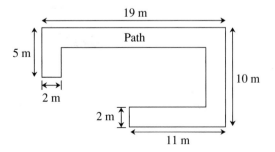

11 🖩 A rectangular room in a school is to be converted into a library. The room is 10.5 m long and 7.5 m wide. It is to be carpeted so that a 2 m wide border is left uncarpeted. The carpet costs £25 a square metre. Find:
a The area of carpet needed.
b The cost of carpeting.

MASTERMINDER

12 🖩 The diagram represents a door 2000 mm high with a rectangular glass panel in it. The area of the door, including the glass, is 1.52 m². The perimeter (the distance around the edge) of the glass is 188 cm.
a Find the width of the door in metres.
b Find the width of the glass, if its height is half the width of the door.

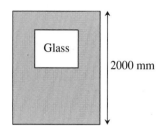

___ Triangles

___ *Activity 30*

1 Draw a rectangle ABCD of length 10 cm and width 6 cm. Draw the diagonal BD as shown here.

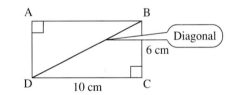

2 With a pair of scissors carefully cut out the triangles ADB and CDB.

3 Look carefully at triangle CDB and explain why each of the triangles on the right has an area of 30 cm².

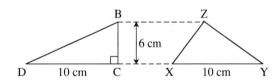

REMEMBER

Area (A) of a triangle = $\frac{1}{2}$ Base (b) × Perpendicular height (h)

$A = \frac{1}{2} \times b \times h$

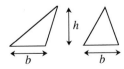

(Perpendicular means 'at right angles to')

■*EXAMPLE 3*

A triangle has an area of $18.7\,\text{cm}^2$. Find its perpendicular height if its base is $6.8\,\text{cm}$.

[F] $A = 18.7\text{ cm}^2$

h

6.8 cm

[E] $\text{Area} = \dfrac{1}{2} \times b \times h$

[S] $18.7 = \dfrac{1}{2} \times 6.8 \times h$

[W] $18.7 = 3.4h$ (Divide both sides by 3.4)

$\dfrac{18.7}{3.4} = h$

$h = 5.5\text{ cm}$ (Don't forget the units)

■*EXAMPLE 4*

Draw x and y axes and plot the points A (2, 0), B (2, −2), C (−2, −2), D (−2, 0), E (−1, 2).
Join up the points to make a five-sided figure.
Find its area, giving your answer in square units.

[F]

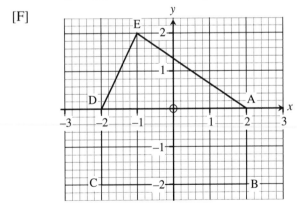

[E]   Area of ABCDE = Area ABCD + Area ADE

[S] $= (4 \times 2) + (\frac{1}{2} \times 4 \times 2)$

[W] $= 8 + 4$

$= 12$ square units

___ Exercise 45

1 Find the area of a triangle when its base length is 14 cm and its perpendicular height is:
   a 8 cm   **b** 5.4 cm   **c** 3.7 cm

2 Find the area of a triangle when its perpendicular height is 9 cm and its base length is:
   a 12 cm   **b** 5.8 cm   **c** 7.7 cm

3 Find the area of a triangle when its base length is 9.6 m and its perpendicular height is:
   a 4.65 m   **b** 9.4 m   **c** 59 cm

For Questions 4 to 8, find either the base length (b) or the perpendicular height (h).

4 Area = 60 cm^2 **5** Area = 45 cm^2 **6** Area = 31.6 cm^2

7 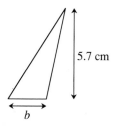 Area = 3.705 cm^2 **8** 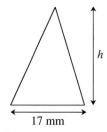 Area = 15.64 cm^2

9 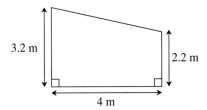 The diagram represents the end of a garden shed. Find its area.

10 The diagram represents the end of a large factory building. Find its area.

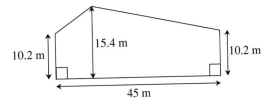

For each of the Questions 11 to 14, draw x and y axes from 3 to -3, using the same scale on both axes. Plot the points and join them up to form a shape. Find the area, in square units, of the shape.

11 A $(1, 2)$, B $(2, -1)$, C $(2, -3)$, D $(-2, -3)$, E $(-2, -1)$

12 A $(2, 3)$, B $(-3, 0)$, C $(-3, -3)$, D $(2, -3)$

13 A $(3, 0)$, B $(2, 2)$, C $(1, 0)$, D $(0, 2)$, E $(-1, 0)$, F $(-2, 2)$, G $(-3, 0)$, H $(-3, -3)$, I $(3, -3)$

MASTERMINDERS

14 A $(-3, 3)$, B $(0, 3)$, C $(1, 1)$, D $(3, 1)$, E $(3, 0)$, F $(1, -2)$, G $(-1, -2)$, H $(-3, -3)$

15 ▦ The broken line indicates the line of symmetry. Find the value of x if the area of the figure is 20.4 cm².

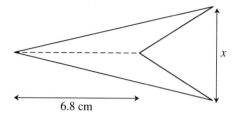

6.8 cm

___ **8.3** Volume

Volume is a measure of the space taken up by a solid. Volume is measured in cubic units, the most common being cubic millimetres (mm³), cubic centimetres (cm³) and cubic metres (m³).

A cuboid is a 'box shape' with rectangular shaped sides. The volume of a cuboid is found by multiplying the length by the breadth by the height.

___ REMEMBER

- Volume (V) of a cuboid = Length (l) × Breadth (b) × Height (h)
- Base area (A) = Length (l) × Breadth (b)

$V = lbh$

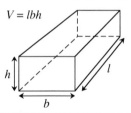

■EXAMPLE 1 ▦

The volume of a cuboid is 87.78 cm³. Find its breadth, if it is 5.5 cm long and 4.2 cm high.

[F] See diagram.

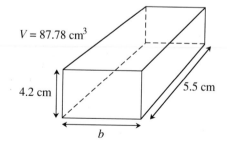

$V = 87.78$ cm³

4.2 cm   5.5 cm

b

[E] $V = lbh$

[S] $87.78 = 5.5 \times b \times 4.2$

[W] $87.78 = 23.1b$ (Divide both sides by 23.1)

$$\frac{87.78}{23.1} = b$$

$b = 3.8$ cm

___ Exercise 46

For Questions 1 to 10, V is the volume of the cuboid, A is its base area, l its length, b its breadth and h its height.

1 $l = 25$ cm, $b = 5$ cm, $h = 8$ cm. Find V.

2 $A = 240$ mm^2, $h = 15$ mm. Find V.

3 $l = 25$ cm, $b = 60$ cm, $V = 7500$ cm^3. Find h.

4 $b = 10$ m, $h = 18$ m, $V = 4500$ m^3. Find l.

5 $l = 125$ cm, $h = 28$ cm, $V = 21\,000$ cm^3. Find b.

6 ▦ $l = 12.5$ cm, $b = 2.4$ cm, $V = 105$ cm^3. Find h.

7 ▦ $l = 14.4$ cm, $h = 12.5$ cm, $V = 738$ cm^3. Find b.

8 ▦ $A = 8$ mm^2, $h = 1.7$ mm. Find V.

9 ▦ $A = 23.4$ cm^2, $V = 70.2$ cm^3. Find h.

10 ▦ $h = 9.4$ cm, $V = 169.2$ cm^3. Find A.

11 The picture shows a rectangular carton of tomato juice.
  a Find its total surface area.
  b Find its volume.
  c How many 75 cm^3 glasses can be filled from this carton?

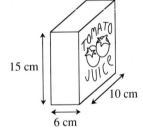

15 cm

10 cm

6 cm

12 A small carton of orange juice has a base area of 25 cm^2 and a volume of 200 cm^3.
  a Find its height.
  b How many cartons of orange juice would be needed to fill a container which has a volume of half a cubic metre?

13 ▦ A book is the shape of a cuboid. Its front cover has an area of 504 cm^2 and its volume is 756 cm^3.
  a Find its thickness.
  b How many books would there be in a pile 2.25 m high?

14 ▦ A pad of paper contains 100 individual sheets. Each sheet is 21 cm by 29.5 cm by 0.1 mm.
  a Find the volume of one sheet of paper.
  b Find the thickness of the pad.
  c Find the number of sheets of paper needed to cover a football pitch of area 9000 m^2. Give your answer to the nearest thousand.

15 ▦ A certain copy of *The Times* has 24 numbered pages. The front page measures 37 cm by 60 cm and has a volume of 13.32 cm^3.
  a Find the volume of the whole newspaper.
  b The copy is folded into four. How many similarly folded copies would be needed to make a pile 100 m high?

16 🖩 The largest scientific building in the world (by volume) is the Vehicle Assembly Building (VAB) at the Kennedy Space Centre in Florida. It is 158 m wide, 218 m long and 160 m high.

Investigate the size of this enormous building by comparing it to the volume of your school hall.

MASTERMINDERS

17 🖩 A wooden box has a length of 48 cm, a width of 30 cm and a depth of 10 cm. A cardboard box has a length which is shorter than the wooden box in the ratio 5 : 8 and a width which is narrower in the ratio 3 : 5, but it is deeper in the ratio 3 : 2. Find the volume of the cardboard box.

18 (You may **not** use a calculator for this question.)

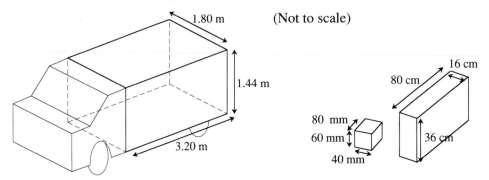

a How many small boxes can be packed into the larger box?
b How many large boxes can be packed into the van?
c What is the largest number of small boxes which can be packed into the van?

— 8.4 Speed

One unit of speed is 'miles per hour' (mph). It can be written 'miles/hour'. This reminds us that speed is measured by dividing the distance travelled (d) by the time taken (t), that is, d/t or $\frac{d}{t}$.

In Physics speed is denoted by the letter 'v'. In this book we will also use 'v' to represent speed.

> ### — REMEMBER
>
> Mean (average) speed (v) in miles per hour = $\dfrac{\text{Distance travelled } (d) \text{ in miles}}{\text{Time taken } (t) \text{ in hours}} = \dfrac{d}{t}$

Other common units of speed are km/h and cm/s. However, when measuring very slow speeds a unit of cm/year could be used. This might be sensible when measuring, for example, the rate at which a cliff is being eroded by the sea.

1776 1886 1904

1912 1919 1919

On the other hand, to measure the speed of light (nothing can travel faster) a unit of km/s is normally used. Light travels at about 300 000 km/s.

When using the equation $v = \frac{d}{t}$ you must be careful not to mix the units. For example, if the speed is given in m/s, the distance must be in metres and the time must be in seconds.

■ EXAMPLE 1

A car in the 24-hour Le Mans motor race travelled 2420 miles. Find its mean speed to the nearest whole number.

[F] $d = 2420$ miles, $t = 24$ hours

[E] $v = \dfrac{d}{t}$

[S] $v = \dfrac{2420}{24}$ miles/hour

[W] $= 101$ miles/hour, to the nearest whole number

■ EXAMPLE 2

A train travelled at a mean speed of 150 km/h for 3.5 hours. How far did it travel?

[F] $v = 150$ km/h, $t = 3.5$ hours

[E] $v = \dfrac{d}{t}$

[S] $150 = \dfrac{d}{3.5}$ (Multiply both sides by 3.5)

[W] $3.5 \times 150 = d$

  $d = 525$ km

■ EXAMPLE 3

The train from Moscow to Vladivostock travels at a mean speed of 28 miles/hour for the 6300 miles. How long does it take **a** in hours **b** in days to the nearest day?

[F] $d = 6300$ miles, $v = 28$ miles/hour

[E] $v = \dfrac{d}{t}$

[S] $28 = \dfrac{6300}{t}$ (Multiply both sides by t)

[W] $28 \times t = 6300$ (Divide both sides by 28)

  $t = \dfrac{6300}{28}$

  $= 225$ hours

  $= \dfrac{225}{24} = 9.375$ days

  $= 9$ days to the nearest day

___ Exercise 47

1 An aeroplane travels 4050 miles. Find its mean speed if it takes:
  a 5 hours   **b** 9 hours   **c** 15 hours

2 A motor cyclist rides at a mean speed of 120 km/hour. Find how far he travels in:
  a 2 hours   **b** 1.5 hours   **c** 0.8 hour

3 A model speedboat race takes place over a 210 m course. Find the time taken by a boat if it completes the course at a mean speed of:
  a 15 m/s   **b** 14 m/s   **c** 12 m/s

For Questions 4 to 10, v is the mean speed, d is the distance and t is the time.

4 $d = 280$ m, $t = 56$ s. Find v.

5 $v = 38$ cm/s, $t = 4.2$ s. Find d.

6 $d = 97.5$ km, $v = 13$ km/h. Find t.

7 $v = 15$ miles/h, $d = 133.5$ miles. Find t in hours and minutes.

8 🖩 $d = 405$ km, $t = 5.4$ h. Find v.

9 🖩 $v = 75$ miles/h, $t = 4$ h 30 minutes. Find d.

10 🖩 $v = 14.2$ m/s, $d = 78.1$ m. Find t.

11 One of the highest speeds of any space vehicle was that achieved by Pioneer II on its way to Saturn in 1974. During its flight it travelled 541 300 miles in five hours. Find its mean speed.

12 The Earth travels around the Sun once every year. If it travels at a mean speed of 64 500 miles/hour, how far does it travel in 24 hours?

13 An American space shuttle reaches a speed of 28 000 km/h during its launch. If this speed could be maintained, how long would it take to reach the Moon which is 378 000 km away?

14 A bullet is fired from a gun at 1600 m/s and it hits the target after 0.15 second. How far was the target from the gun?

15 Light travels at 300 000 kilometres per second. Calculate the distance light will travel in one minute. How many times could light travel around the Earth in one minute if the distance around the Earth is 40 000 km?

16 🖩 An InterCity express train has a top speed of 200 km/h. If it could maintain this speed, find how long it would take to travel from London to Bristol, a distance of 190 km. Give your answer in minutes.

17 🖩 The aeroplane 'Voyager' circled the Earth nonstop in December 1986. This journey of 24 987 miles took 216 hours. Find its mean speed (to the nearest whole mile per hour).

18 🔢 This is part of a railway timetable. Find, to the nearest whole number, the mean speed of the train from:
a Glasgow to Stranraer.
b Ayr to Barrhill.
c Paisley to Girvan.

Miles	Station	Time
0	Glasgow	08:57
7.25	Paisley	09:08
26.75	Kilwinning	09:27
41.5	Ayr	09:52
50.5	Maybole	10:05
62.75	Girvan	10:23
75	Barrhill	10:45
101	Stranraer	11:25

MASTERMINDERS

19 🔢 The speed at which a human hair grows is 0.43 mm/day. The speed at which human fingernail grows is 0.07 mm/day.
a Find the length that each will grow in 365 days.
b Write each of the above answers as a speed in cm/year.
c How many times faster does human hair grow than human finger nails?
d Approximately how long would each grow in 100 years?

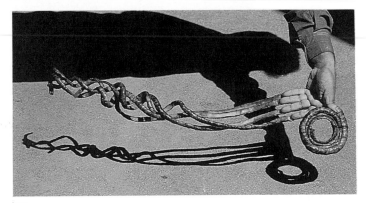

20 🔢 Find the missing quantities in the table of world records below. Give each answer in the units shown. After ≈ give the approximate answer.

		Mode of transport	Mean speed	Time taken	Distance covered
a	(i)	Jet-engined car	17 km/min	5 min	☐ km
	(ii)	(Richard Noble) UK	1020 km/h	☐ h	255 km
	(iii)		≈ ☐ m/s	60 s	17 000 m
b	(i)	Bicycle	68 m/s	30 s	☐ m
	(ii)	(John Howard) USA	152 mph	☐ h	114 miles
	(iii)		≈ ☐ km/min	3 min	8.6 miles
c	(i)	Aircraft (SR-71A)	36.55 miles/min	☐ min	73.1 miles
	(ii)	USA	2193 mph	$\frac{2}{3}$ hr	☐ miles
	(iii)		≈ ☐ km/s	3600 sec	3530 km

Activity 31

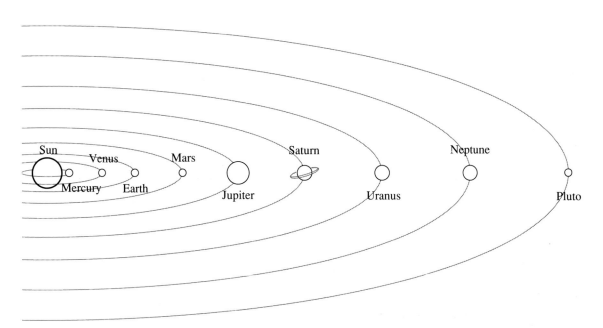

The nine planets in our Solar System rotate around the Sun. The time (t) it takes for light to reach us, on Earth, from the Sun and each of the other eight planets is shown in the table.

Heavenly object	t (minutes)
Sun	8
Mercury	5
Venus	2
Mars	4
Jupiter	35
Saturn	73
Uranus	151
Neptune	241
Pluto	325

1 The following equation gives the distance (d), in millions of kilometres, that light travels in time (t) in minutes:

$$d = \frac{t}{0.056}$$

Work out the value of d, to the nearest whole number, for each of the times shown in the table. Put your results in a table.

2 Using a scale of 1 mm to 20 million km, make a scale drawing to illustrate the distance each planet is from the Sun.

141

▁▁ Revision Exercise 8A

Calculators are **not allowed**.

1 Simplify:
   a $4a + 3a$ **b** $6x - 2x$ **c** $x + x + x$ **d** $4y + x - y$
2 Solve for x:
   a $2x = 10$ **b** $\frac{x}{2} = 10$ **c** $2 = \frac{10}{x}$ **d** $2 + x = 10$
3 The diagram shows a rectangular
   swimming pool surrounded by a patio.
   Find the area of the patio.

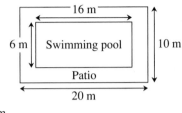

4 If the area of the triangle is $8.2\,\text{cm}^2$, find
   the base length AB.

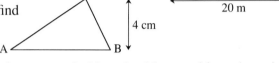

5 A book is in the shape of a cuboid. Its front cover is $10\,\text{cm}$ by $15\,\text{cm}$ and its volume is $300\,\text{cm}^3$.
   a Find its thickness.
   b Find its total surface area.
6 An InterCity train averages 120 miles per hour.
   a How far does it travel in $2\frac{1}{2}$ hours?
   b How long does it take to travel 420 miles?

▁▁ Revision Exercise 8B

Calculators are **not allowed**.

1 Simplify if possible:
   a $a + a + a + a$ **b** $3a + 2b - 3c$ **c** $3a - 2b + 3b$ **d** $4x - 6x + 2x$
2 Solve for x:
   a $42 = \frac{x}{7}$ **b** $42 = \frac{7}{x}$ **c** $42 = x + 4.2$ **d** $4 - x = 42$
3 The area of this letter 'L' is $30\,\text{cm}^2$.
   Find the width, x, in centimetres.

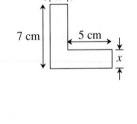

4 The area of the triangle is $72\,\text{mm}^2$.
   Find the height.

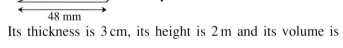

5 A door is in the shape of a cuboid. Its thickness is $3\,\text{cm}$, its height is $2\,\text{m}$ and its volume is
   $48\,000\,\text{cm}^3$. Find its width.
6 An InterCity train averages 120 miles per hour.
   a How far does it travel in 2 hours and 20 minutes?
   b How long does it take to travel 42 miles?

Basics Test 8

A Calculator

    1 Find the mean of: 2.09, 3.8, 4.79, 6.8   **2** Work out: $67 \div 0.308$ to the nearest 10

    3 Solve for a: $6.9 + a = 11.86$ **4** Solve for b: $45.8 = b - 98$

    5 Solve for c: $78.4 = \frac{c}{9}$ **6** Solve for d: $224d = 784$

B Paper and pencil

    7 Simplify $x + x + x + x + x$ **8** Simplify $7a - 9a + 10a$

    9 $\frac{3}{8} + \frac{1}{6}$ **10** $\frac{5}{8} \div \frac{2}{3}$

    11 Write 12 minutes as a decimal of an hour.

    12 16% of 25   **13** Solve for e: $7 = \frac{4.9}{e}$

    14 Solve for f: $17.03 - f = 9.4$ **15** Reduce $\frac{144}{180}$ to its lowest terms.

C Mental

    Ten questions will be read out to you. Use the following facts to answer Questions 16 to 20:

      $a = 4, \quad b = 12, \quad c = 0.2$

Puzzlers

1   The next person you meet is likely to have more than the average number of legs. Comment

2   This problem is about arranging dots so that there are a certain number in each row. For example, the diagram shows how 4 dots can be arranged in 6 rows so that there are 2 dots in each row.

    Draw separate diagrams to show how 9 dots can be arranged in:

    a 8 rows with 3 dots in each row.

    b 9 rows with 3 dots in each row.

    c 10 rows with 3 dots in each row. (It is believed that Sir Isaac Newton was the first person to have discovered the last arrangement.)

3   Find the number which represents each of the letters in each of the following:

    a
```
   S P E N D
 -   M O R E
 ───────────
   M O N E Y
```
    b
```
   C R O S S
 + R O A D S
 ───────────
   D A N G E R
```
    c
```
   F O U R
   T W O
 + O N E
 ─────────
   S E V E N
```

Coursework: Jigsaw edging

Toby is doing a 1000-piece jigsaw puzzle.
He asks 'How many edging pieces are there?'
We investigate the answer to his question.

If Toby's puzzle had no more than 25 pieces and there were more than two pieces on any one side, there would be ten different arrangements to his puzzle. Three of these arrangements are shown below, with the arrangement of pieces given in brackets.

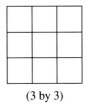

(3 by 3)

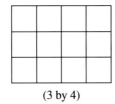

(3 by 4)

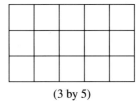

(3 by 5)

1   Copy these arrangements and draw the other seven possible arrangements. Write down all ten arrangements, in brackets, in a logical order.

2   In each of the ten arrangements count:
   a The total number of pieces.
   b The number of edging pieces.
   c The number of non-edging pieces.

3   Copy and complete the table below with your results:

Arrangement of puzzle	Total number of pieces	Number of edging pieces	Number of non-edging pieces
(3 by 3)	9	8	1
(3 by 4)			

EXTENSION

4   **a** If the arrangement of pieces of a puzzle is (*a* by *b*), explain why the number of edging pieces (*N*) is given by the following equation:

   $N = 2a + 2b - 4$

   b Use this equation to find out the number of possible edging pieces in Toby's 1000-piece puzzle. Explain why the equation does not produce a sensible answer to one possible arrangement of the puzzle.

9 ARITHMETIC III

9.1 Cubes and cube roots

The 'square of 6' is written 6^2 and means 6×6.

The 'square root of 36' is written $\sqrt{36}$ and equals the number which, when multiplied by itself, gives 36.

In the next Activity we explore the relationship between the side length of a cube and its volume, and vice versa.

Activity 32

In Chapter 8, you found that the volume of a cuboid = Length × Breadth × Height

1 In a cube the length, breadth and height all have the same value. The volume of a cube of side length 5 cm is shown here.

Volume of cube

$= 5 \times 5 \times 5$

$= 5^3$ — 'Five cubed'

$= 125 \text{ cm}^3$

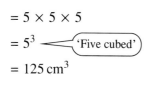

Copy and complete the table:

Cube	
Side length (cm)	Volume (cm³)
1	
2	
3	
4	
5	$5 \times 5 \times 5 = 5^3 = 125$
6	

2 If we are given the volume of a cube we can find its side length. To do this we 'cube root' its volume. This means that we must find the number which, when multiplied by itself and by itself again, gives the volume.

For example, given a cube of volume 216 cm^3, the side length can be found as follows:

Volume = 216 cm³

Side length

$= \sqrt[3]{216}$ — 'Cube root' of 216

$= 6 \text{ cm}$

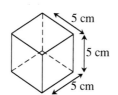

a Copy and complete the table:

Cube	
Volume (cm³)	Side length (cm)
1	
8	
27	
64	
125	
216	$\sqrt[3]{216} = 6$
343	
512	
729	
1000	

(Check: $6 \times 6 \times 6 = 216$)

b Investigate how you can use your calculator, **without using the cube root button**, to find the side length of a cube with a volume of 20 cm^3. Briefly describe your method.

__ 9.2 Indices

In the previous section we explained that $5 \times 5 \times 5$ could be written 5^3.

> The 3, written in this position, is called an 'index'.
> The plural is 'indices'.

Other numbers can be written using indices. For example:

1    $32 = 2 \times 2 \times 2 \times 2 \times 2 = 2^5$

2    $81 = 3 \times 3 \times 3 \times 3 = 3^4$

These two examples are shown in the table in Exercise 48.

__ Exercise 48 ▦

Copy and complete the following tables.

	Product form	Index form	Result
1	$2 \times 2 \times 2 \times 2 \times 2$	2^5	32
2	$3 \times 3 \times 3 \times 3$	3^4	81
3	$2 \times 2 \times 2 \times 2$		
4	$7 \times 7 \times 7 \times 7$		
5	9×9		
6		4^4	
7		6^3	
8		11^3	
9		1^3	
10			121
11			125
12			243

MASTERMINDERS

	Product form	Index form	Result
13		1.2^3	
14			0.008
15			0.002 43

16 **Investigate** how many ways the number 4096 can be written using index form.

9.3 Multiples and factors

Multiples

3, 6, 9, 12 and 15 are all multiples of 3, because all of these numbers are **exactly divisible** by 3.

■ *EXAMPLE 1*

List the first five multiples of **a** 8 and **b** 15.

a   8, 16, 24, 32 and 40
b   15, 30, 45, 60 and 75

Exercise 49

List the first five multiples of each of the following:

1 5	**2** 4	**3** 20	**4** 25	**5** 16

List the first five multiples of each of the following.

6 ▦ 32	**7** ▦ 35	**8** ▦ 77	**9** ▦ 251	**10** ▦ 129

Factors

1, 2, 3, 4, 6 and 12 are all factors of 12, because 12 can be **divided exactly** by each one of these numbers.

■ *EXAMPLE 2*

List the factors of **a** 15 and **b** 36.

a   1, 3, 5 and 15
b   1, 2, 3, 4, 6, 9, 12, 18 and 36

Exercise 50

List the factors of each of the following:

1 6	**2** 39	**3** 32	**4** 75	**5** 40
6 54	**7** 48	**8** 60	**9** 90	**10** 84

__ 9.4 Prime numbers and prime factors

__ Prime numbers

A prime number is a number which has no factors apart from 1 and itself. (The number 1 is not a prime.) For example, 3 is a prime number because only 1 and 3 will divide exactly into it.

The only **even** number which is prime is 2 since all other even numbers are divisible by 2. Therefore all prime numbers greater than 2 are odd numbers.

__ *Activity 33*

In this Activity we use the method which Eratosthenes devised to find prime numbers. (Eratosthenes was a Greek mathematician (about 276–194 BC) who is reputed to have calculated the circumference of the Earth to within 200 m.)

1   Copy this table:

	2	3	4	5	6	7	8	9	10
11	12	13	14	15	16	17	18	19	20
21	22	23	24	25	26	27	28	29	30
31	32	33	34	35	36	37	38	39	40
41	42	43	44	45	46	47	48	49	50
51	52	53	54	55	56	57	58	59	60
61	62	63	64	65	66	67	68	69	70
71	72	73	74	75	76	77	78	79	80
81	82	83	84	85	86	87	88	89	90
91	92	93	94	95	96	97	98	99	100
101	102	103	104	105	106	107	108	109	110
111	112	113	114	115	116	117	118	119	120

   a Put a circle around 2, the smallest prime. Cross out all **multiples** of 2 because these cannot be primes.

   b Put a circle around 3, the second smallest prime. Cross out all **multiples** of 3 because these, also, cannot be primes.

   c Continue circling primes and crossing out multiples of primes until only primes remain on your table.

2   List all the primes less than 120.

___ Prime factors

All numbers which are **not** primes can be written as the products of primes.

For example, 39 can be written as the product of the primes 3 and 13:

39 = 3 × 13

■ *EXAMPLE 1*

Express each of the following as a product of prime factors:
a 42 **b** 858 **c** 48

a 42 = 2 × 21

$\qquad$ = 2 × 3 × 7

b 858 = 2 × 429

$\qquad$ = 2 × 3 × 143

$\qquad$ = 2 × 3 × 11 × 13

c 48 = 3 × 16

$\qquad$ = 3 × 2 × 8

$\qquad$ = 3 × 2 × 2 × 4

$\qquad$ = 3 × 2 × 2 × 2 × 2

Since 2 × 2 × 2 × 2 can be written 2^4, the product of the factors of 48 can be written 3×2^4.

___ Exercise 51

Express each of the following as a product of prime factors, using indices where necessary:

1 30	**2** 66	**3** 210	**4** 390
5 770	**6** 2618	**7** 165	**8** 399
9 1155	**10** 715	**11** 6545	**12** 340
13 40	**14** 54	**15** 216	**16** 900

17 ▦ 6125

18 ▦ 41 503

19 ▦ 48 841

20 ▦ 54 060

__ 9.5 Sequences

A series of numbers which follows a definite pattern is called a 'sequence'.
Examples of sequences are:

Counting numbers: 1,   2,   3,   4,   5,   ...

Even numbers: 2,   4,   6,   8,   10, ...

Multiples of 5:   5,   10, 15, 20,   ...

Cubes: 1,   8,   27, 64, ...

Many different problems in Mathematics can be solved by investigating the pattern in a sequence of numbers. The next Activity is a good example.

__ *Activity 34* ▦

Investigate the claim by the author of this book that he can trace one line of his direct ancestors, through 29 generations, back to William the Conqueror. (A 'direct ancestor' is a parent, a grandparent, a great-grandparent, etc.)

Like many complicated problems, we must first simplify it, then establish a rule, and finally use the rule to solve the problem.

1 Copy and continue this diagram for another two generations.

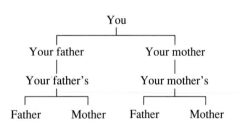

2 Copy this table and use your diagram to help complete it.

Generations back	Number of direct ancestors in that generation
1	$2 = 2^1$
2	$4 = 2^2$
3	
4	
5	
6	
n	

3   Use the last entry in your table to work out the number of direct ancestors of the author, 29 generations back. Give your answer to the nearest 1000. Comment.

■ EXAMPLE 1

In the sequence, 4, 8, 12, 16, ..., find:

a the fifth and sixth terms   **b** the rule for the nth term   **c** the 30th term.

a The fifth term $= 16 + 4 = 20$
The sixth term $= 20 + 4 = 24$
(This is because each term is 4 more than the previous term.)

b To find the nth term, put the given sequence into a 'sequence table' so that the relationship between each term in the sequence and its term number can be seen.

Term number	1	2	3	4
Sequence	4	8	12	16

Because each term in the sequence is 4 times larger than its term number, the nth term is $4n$.

c The 30th term is found by substituting $n = 30$.

30th term $= 4 \times 30 = 120$

___ Activity 35

It is important for you to be able to produce a sequence from a given set of instructions. This flow diagram shows how the first four terms of a sequence can be produced.

Use the flow diagram to show that when $X = 4$ and $P = 1$, the sequence produced is 5, 6, 7, 8.

Now use it to produce the following sequences. In each case put your sequence in a sequence table and write down the rule for the nth term.

1 $X = 2, P = 1$

2 $X = 3, P = 1$

3 $X = 0, P = 2$

4 $X = 0, P = 3$

5 $X = 5, P = 1$

6 $X = 0, P = 5$

Comment on your results.

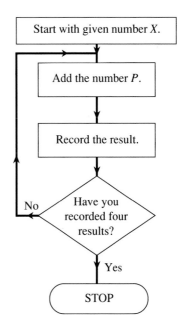

> *REMEMBER*
>
> - **To continue a sequence:** look for a pattern and if necessary work out the difference between successive terms.
> - **To find the rule of the nth term:** use the sequence table.

▬ Exercise 52

For Questions 1 to 10, find the next two terms.

1 4, 9, 14, 19, 24, ..., ...

2 4, 9, 15, 22, 30, ..., ...

3 9, 11, 15, 21, 29, ..., ...

4 2, 4, 8, 16, 32, ..., ...

5 40, 50, 59, 67, 74, ..., ...

6
```
          ***
     **   ***
*    **   ***
1,   4,   9,   ..., ...
```

7
```
           *
      *   **
*    **   ***
1,   3,   6,   ..., ...
```

8 2, 3, 7, 16, 32, ..., ...

9 8, 10, 13, 18, 26, ..., ...

10 12, 15, 11, 16, 10, ..., ...

For Questions 11 to 19, find **a** the nth term, **b** the 25th term.

11 5, 10, 15, 20, ...

12 7, 14, 21, 28, ...

13 6, 7, 8, 9, ...

14 9, 10, 11, 12, ...

15 8, 16, 24, 32, ...

16 11, 12, 13, 14, ...

17 12, 24, 36, 48, ...

18 1, 4, 9, 16, ...

19 1, 8, 27, 64, ...

20 This is part of a brick wall.

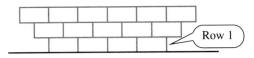

Row 1

Copy and complete the table.

How many bricks would there be in
a the nth row   **b** the 21st row?

Row number	Number of bricks
1	4
2	5
3	
4	
5	
6	

21 Copy and complete the table.
   a Write down the sum of the first n odd numbers.
   b What is the sum of the first 100 odd numbers?
   c How many consecutive odd numbers add up to 169?

No. of odd numbers	Working	Total
1	1	1
2	1 + 3	4
3	1 + 3 + 5	
4		
5		
6		

22 The results of an experiment are:

x	2	4		8	10
y	5	9	13		21

Copy and complete the table.

23 This is part of a pattern made with matches.

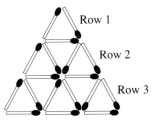

Row 1

Row 2

Row 3

Row	No. of matches	No. of triangles
1	3	1
2	6	3
3		
4		
5		
6		

Copy and complete the table.

   a Find the number of matches in the nth row and hence the number of matches in the 30th row.
   b Show that the number of triangles in the nth row is $2n - 1$. Use this to find the row number in which there are 31 triangles.

MASTERMINDERS

24 Find the next two terms in the sequence: 12, 23, 44, 85, 166, . . .

25 Find the nth term in the sequences: **a** 5, 7, 9, 11, . . . **b** 1, 4, 7, 10, . . .

26 Find the sum of the first 100 even counting numbers.

___ Revision Exercise 9A

Calculators are **not allowed**.

1 Copy and complete this table:

	Product form	Index form	Result
a	$2 \times 2 \times 2$		
b		3^2	
c			100

2 A cube has a volume of $27\,\text{cm}^3$. What is its side length?
3 List the first four multiples of 3.
4 List the seven factors of 100.
5 Express 70 as the product of prime factors.
6 Find the next term in the sequence: 8, 10, 13, 17, ...
7 Find the nth term in the sequence: 5, 10, 15, 20, ...
8 The diagram shows the bottom two rows of a 'House of Cards'. In the first row there are 17 cards and in the second row there are 14 cards.
   a How many cards must there be in the fourth row?
   b How many cards would be needed to complete the 'House of Cards'?

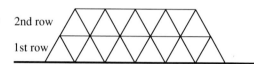

2nd row
1st row

___ Revision Exercise 9B

Calculators are **not allowed**.

1 Write the following in index form:
   a $1 \times 1 \times 1 \times 1$ **b** $3.8 \times 3.8 \times 3.8$ **c** 25 **d** 128
2 A cube has a volume of $27\,\text{cm}^3$. Find its total surface area.
3 The numbers 8, 16, 24, 32 are the first four multiples of which number?
4 List the 12 factors of 150.
5 Express 585 as the product of prime factors.
6 Find the next two terms in these sequences:
   a 1, 3, 7, 15, 31, ..., ...
   b 21, 23, 20, 24, 19, ..., ...
7 The nth term in a sequence is $2n + 1$. Find the value of the eighth term.
8 The results of an experiment are as shown here: Copy and complete this table.

x	3	6		12	15
y	8		26	35	44

9 The diagram shows a pyramid made with 30 snowballs. It is four layers high. How many layers would there be in a pyramid, built in the same way, with a total of 285 snowballs?

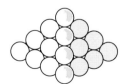

▬ Basics Test 9

A Calculator

   1 Solve for a: $31.2 + a = 49.02$

   2 Solve for b: $\frac{b}{2.6} = 8$

   3 Solve for c: $9c = 16.2$

   4 Solve for d: $d - 9.043 = 1.608$

   5 Find the mean of 1.3, 1.7, 2.2 and 6.4.

   6 Find $(1.3)^3$ to the nearest tenth.

B Paper and pencil

   7 $3.2 - 0.024$

   8 $2.537 + 0.215 - 1.352$

   9 Find 28% of 300 km.

   10 Change $\frac{33}{40}$ to a percentage.

   11 Simplify $2a + a + 2a$.

   12 Find the missing number: $\frac{7.5}{?} = 10$.

   13 What fraction of an hour is 17 minutes?

   14 $64.6 \div 17$

   15 Work out an approximate answer to $\frac{39.87 \times 18.7}{4.9}$.

C Mental

Ten questions will be read out to you. Use the following facts for questions 16 to 20:

$$p = \tfrac{1}{2}, \quad q = \tfrac{1}{3}, \quad r = \tfrac{1}{4}$$

▬ Puzzlers

1 After a power cut from 09:00 hours to 12:00 hours, the electric clock restarted immediately, but went backwards at the usual rate. In the evening, however, at a certain time it gave the correct time. What was this time?

2 The diagram shows a street plan with 16 blocks of housing. The problem is to find how many different routes a car can take from the junction at X to the junction at A if it can only travel North or East. For example, from B it can travel by two different routes and both these are shown on the diagram.

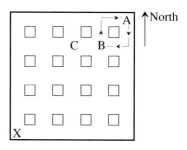

   a Copy the diagram and mark in three different routes which the car can take from C to A.

   b On your diagram at each junction, write down the number of different routes which the car can take to A. (Start near to A.)

   c What has the sequence 1, 4, 10, 20, ... to do with this problem?

   d Continue the sequence 1, 5, 15, 35, ... for another three terms.

   e Explore a similar problem with (i) 25 (ii) 36 blocks of housing.

Coursework: Primes and factors

A few years ago a computer at the University of California was given a program to find the largest prime number. After over eight weeks of nonstop searching it produced

$$2^{44\,497} - 1$$

This number is so large that to write it out in full you would have to write 13 395 digits! However, the Greek mathematician Euclid, who lived between 200 and 300 BC, proved that there are even larger prime numbers.

(*Note*: you will need a calculator for this Coursework.)

1 **a** Write down the number 1 234 000 000. Measure its length. Use your answer to work out the likely length of a 13 395-digit number.
   b If you wrote one digit each second, work out (to the nearest hour) how long it would take you to write out a 13 395-digit number.

2 Find all the factors of the numbers between 2 and 30 inclusive. Copy, extend and complete the table below. If the number is a prime, write 'prime' in the space. (Remember 1 is not a prime.)

1	2	3	4	5	6	7	8	9	10
	prime	prime	2	prime	2, 3	prime			
11	12	13	14	15	16	17	18	19	20

   a Which numbers have an odd number of factors? Try to explain your answer.
   b Find the factors of (i) 68 (ii) 204 (iii) 504.

3 The following Note gives a method to find the **number** of factors in any given number, including 1 and the number itself. For example, to find the number of factors of 504:

> **NOTE**
>
> $504 = 2 \times 2 \times 2 \times 3 \times 3 \times 7$ (Product of primes)
> $\quad\ = 2^3 \times 3^2 \times 7^1$ (Primes written in index form)
> Number of factors $= (3 + 1) \times (2 + 1) \times (1 + 1) = 24$
> (1 is added to each index and the product gives the number of factors)

   Use this method:
   a To check that you found the correct number of factors in question **2b**.
   b To find the number of factors in (i) 2800 (ii) 1024.

EXTENSION

4 Work out the value of $n^2 - n + 41$ for each of the values of n from 1 to 50 inclusive.
   a Comment on any pattern you see in the results.
   b Explain why each of your answers is a prime number except 1681, 1763, 2021 and 2491.

10 GEOMETRY II

10.1 Triangle construction

The points listed here should be followed for all construction questions.

NOTE

- If a diagram is not given, draw a rough **sketch** and include all the facts. (Do **not** spend too long making this sketch; it is only to help you decide where to start constructing.)
- Use a sharp pencil and do not press too hard.
- Hold your pair of compasses with one hand and leave in all your construction lines.
- Start by drawing a straight line slightly longer than the given length.
- Label the completed figure and write any answers at the side.

■ *EXAMPLE 1*

Construct triangle ABC where AB = 8.2 cm, BC = 5.6 cm and CA = 5.6 cm.

a Measure the angle ACB.

b Measure the perpendicular height of C above AB and hence work out the area of triangle ABC.

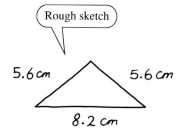

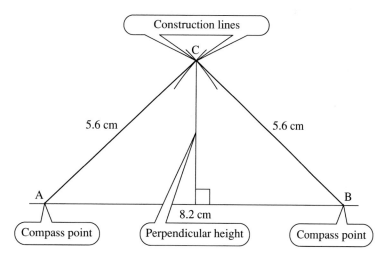

a Angle ACB = 94°

b Height of C above AB
= 3.8 cm
Area of triangle ABC
= $\frac{1}{2} \times 8.2 \times 3.8$
= 16 cm^2
(to the nearest cm^2)

___ Exercise 53

Construct each triangle from the given information. Angles should be measured to the nearest degree and lines measured to the nearest millimetre.

1 Measure AĈB.

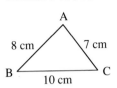

2 Measure XẐY.

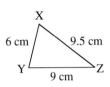

3 Measure NL̂M.

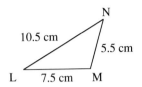

4 Measure ZY.

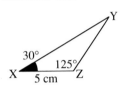

5 Measure RT̂S.

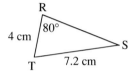

6 Triangle ABC, where AB = 6.3 cm, BC = 4.8 cm and AC = 5.7 cm. Measure angle ABC.

7 Triangle ABC, where AC = 10.7 cm, angle BAC = 47° and angle BCA = 38°. Measure AB.

8 Triangle XYZ, where angle XYZ = 94°, XY = 6.9 cm and YZ = 12.8 cm. Measure XZ.

9 Triangle PQR, where QR = 9.2 cm, QP = 5.8 cm and angle PQR = 85°. Measure angle QPR.

10 Triangle LMN, where LM = 8.7 cm, LN = 8.7 cm and angle MLN = 28°. Measure MN and name the type of triangle LMN.

11 Triangle ABC, where AB = 6 cm, AC = 10 cm and BC = 8 cm. Measure angle ABC and work out the area of the triangle.

12 Triangle ABC, where AB = 7.2 cm, angle CAB = 136° and CB = 14.8 cm. Measure the perpendicular height of A above CB and hence work out the area of the triangle ABC.

13 Triangle XYZ, where XY = 79 mm, angle XYZ = 60° = angle XZY. Measure the perpendicular height of X above YZ and hence work out the area of the triangle XYZ.

14 Triangle ABC, where AC = 7.1 cm, angle BAC = 23° and angle ACB = 117°. Measure the perpendicular height of B above AC and hence work out the area of the triangle ABC.

MASTERMINDERS

15 Triangle ABC, where BC = 8.4 cm, AC = 6 cm and angle ABC = 42°. Measure AB and comment on your result.

16 Triangle ABC, where BC = 10.8 cm, angle ACB = 42° and angle BAC = 92°. Measure AB.

17 Triangle ABC, where BC = 6.5 cm, CA = 4.5 cm and AB = 3.5 cm. Find the position of the point P which is equidistant from BA and BC such that CP = AP. Measure CP.

10.2 Angles of elevation

This diagram shows the **angle of elevation** from a point P to the top of a building.

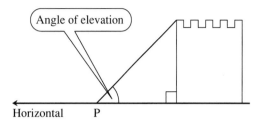

■ *EXAMPLE 1*

Anna measures the angle of elevation to the top of a house and also the distance she is from its base. Her measurements are shown in this sketch.

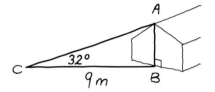

Make a scale drawing of the triangle ABC using a scale of 1 : 100. Use your drawing to estimate the height of the house.

(First scale down the distance of 9 m.)

Actual length   *Drawing*
100 m is represented by 1 m (100 cm)
  1 m is represented by 1 cm
  9 m is represented by 9 cm

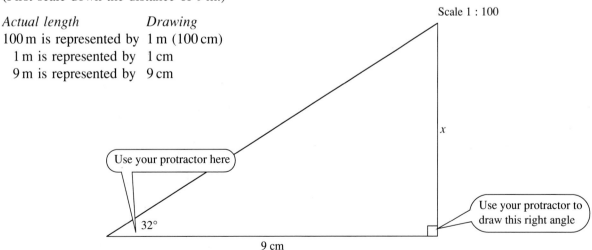

From the drawing, $x = 5.6$ cm, therefore the actual height of the house is 5.6 m.

Exercise 54

For Questions 1 to 5, make a scale drawing of the triangle using a scale of 1 : 200. Measure the height of the triangle and estimate the value of x to the nearest metre.

1

x m

24°

22 m

2

x m

19°

24 m

3

x m

35°

17 m

4

x m

31°

19.6 m

5

x m

42°

18.1 m

For Questions 6 to 8, choose a suitable scale and make a scale drawing to estimate the height of the building to the nearest 10 m. (Note that the angles drawn are not accurate.)

6 Blackpool Tower, UK

7 Empire State Building, USA

8 CN Tower, Canada

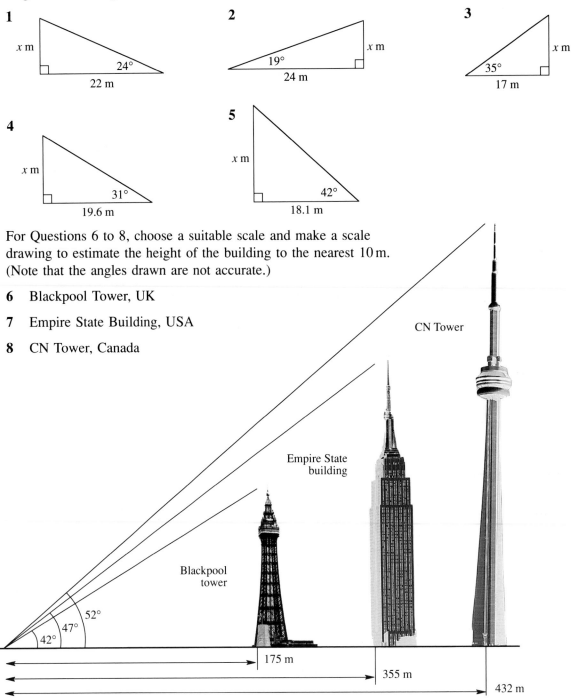

CN Tower

Empire State building

Blackpool tower

52°

47°

42°

175 m

355 m

432 m

___ *Activity 36*

In this Activity you will make a simple 'clinometer' (sometimes called an 'inclinometer') and use it to measure the angle of elevation of a certain building. You will then make a scale drawing and use it to estimate the height of the building.

1 MAKING A SIMPLE CLINOMETER

Materials: A planed piece of wood about 30 cm long which need only be about 2.5 cm by 5 cm
A protractor with a 1.6 mm hole drilled in the middle
A drawing pin

(It is very important that the protractor hangs freely so that it comes to rest in the horizontal position.)

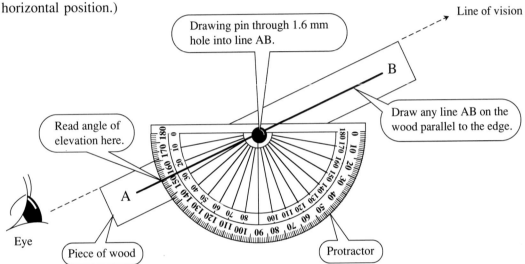

Line of vision

Drawing pin through 1.6 mm hole into line AB.

Draw any line AB on the wood parallel to the edge.

Read angle of elevation here.

Eye

Piece of wood

Protractor

2 USING YOUR CLINOMETER

(You will also need a 30 m tape measure.)

a Choose a suitable building. From a point A use your clinometer to measure the angle of elevation to the top of it. Also measure your distance from the building.

Repeat this from positions B, C, D and E (see diagram). Tabulate your results. Make a suitable scale drawing and use it to estimate the height of the building.

b Comment on the likely accuracy of your result.

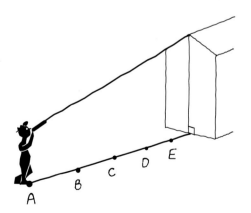

— 10.3 Scale drawing

REMEMBER

- First convert all measurements, using the scale given.
- Use a sharp pencil and do **not** press too hard.
- Use a protractor to draw any right angles.
- Label your drawing and write down the scale used.

■ *EXAMPLE 1*

The sketch shows a rectangular garden with a circular pond in the middle. Make a scale drawing of the garden using a scale of 1 : 200. Find the diagonal length of the garden.

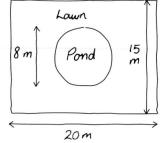

Actual length	*Drawing*
200 m is represented by	1 m (100 cm)
1 m is represented by	$\frac{100}{200} = 0.5$ cm

Pond: 8 m	$0.5 \times 8 = 4$ cm
Lawn: width 15 m	$0.5 \times 15 = 7.5$ cm
length: 20 m	$0.5 \times 20 = 10$ cm

(Note how the centre of the rectangle is found.)

Diagonal of drawing
= 12.5 cm (by measurement)

Actual diagonal of garden
= 12.5 ÷ 0.5 = 25 m

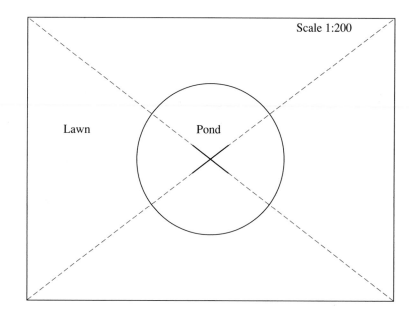

— **Exercise 55**

1 This diagram shows the markings on a tennis court. Use a scale of 1 : 200 to make a scale drawing.
Use your drawing to find the length of the diagonal of the whole court.

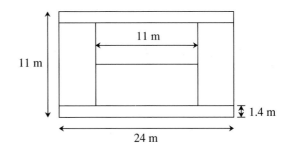

2 Take measurements of your classroom. Choose a suitable scale. Make a scale drawing showing the positions of the windows and the door.

3 This is a site plan of a house, garage and rectangular garden. The dimensions of the house are 10 m by 5 m, and the dimensions of the garage are 6 m by 4 m. Make a scale drawing using a scale of 1 : 200.
Use your drawing to find the length of the diagonal of the garden.

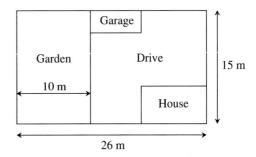

MASTERMINDER

4 The diagram shows a sketch of a full-sized basketball court and the region known as the 'key'.
Use a scale of 1 : 200. Make a scale drawing using the following measurements:

DC = 14 m   AB = 13 m   EF = 6 m   KH = 4.6 m   GK = 1.2 m
IJ = 1.8 m   EO = 1.8 m   ML = 2.35 m   LH = 1.8 m   ON = NM

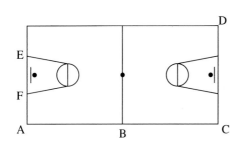

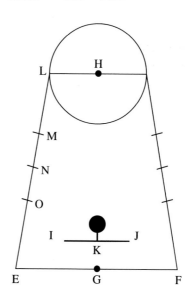

▬ Revision Exercise 10A

1 Construct the triangle from the information given.
  a Measure each of the angles.
  b Measure the perpendicular height of A above BC. Use your answer to work out the area of the triangle.

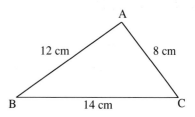

2 From a point P, the angle of elevation is measured to the top of a house. The distance of P to the house is also measured, as shown in the sketch.
  Make a scale drawing of the triangle PXY using a scale of 1 : 100. Use your drawing to estimate the height of the house to the nearest metre.

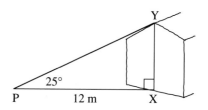

3 The sketch shows a rectangular garden with a semicircular pond at one end.
  Make a scale drawing of the lawn and pond using a scale of 1 : 200. Use your drawing to estimate the length of the diagonal of the lawn to the nearest metre.

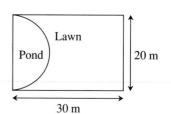

▬ Revision Exercise 10B

1 Construct the triangle from the information given.
  Use any measurements from your drawing to work out the area of the triangle.

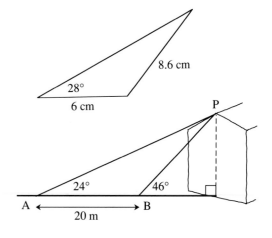

2 The angle of elevation to the top (P) of a building, is taken from two separate places A and B. The sketch shows the details.
  By making a suitable scale drawing, estimate the height of the building to the nearest metre.

3 The diagram shows the lines on a volleyball court.
  DH = 6.7 m
  DG = 11.3 m
  AD = 9 m
  Use these dimensions to make a scale drawing. Use your drawing to estimate the lengths AH and AC to the nearest metre.

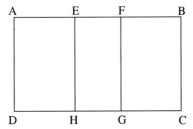

— Basics Test 10

A Calculator

1 Solve for a: $40.23 = 2.98 - a$.

2 Solve for b: $104 = 1.3b$.

3 Solve for c: $7.8 = \frac{c}{9}$.

4 $\frac{0.0096 \times 1.225}{0.112}$

5 Find $(1.2)^4$ to the nearest tenth.

6 Find the mean of 5.2, 4.4, 3.7, 1.6 and 3.1.

B Paper and pencil

7 Simplify $10x - 12x + 14x$.

8 Simplify $14.5y - 9.78y$.

9 Find the missing term: $8 = \frac{104}{?}$.

10 $\frac{1}{3} + \frac{2}{5}$

11 $\frac{3}{5} \div \frac{2}{3}$

12 1.8×0.19

13 $14.82 \div 19$

14 Change 228 minutes to hours and minutes.

15 Approximately how many times does 0.18 divide into 39?

C Mental

Ten questions will be read out to you. Use the following facts for Questions 16 to 20:
Lemonade costs 55p a glass. Crisps cost 17p a packet. Chocolate costs 35p a bar.

— Puzzlers

1 The age of Marcus is between 10 and 99 years inclusive. Reversing the digits of his age gives Rory's age. The difference between their ages is twice Johanna's age. If Rory is ten times as old as Johanna, find their ages.

2 The number 7 can be written using the digit 4 in the following way:

$$4 + \sqrt{4} + \frac{4}{4} = 7$$

Write down how all the numbers, from 1 to 10 inclusive, can be written using only the digit 4 and writing it exactly four times for each number.

3 The diagram shows nine dots in the form of a square. Copy these dots and draw four **straight** lines to pass through all the dots, **without** taking your pencil off the paper.

$$\bullet \quad \bullet \quad \bullet$$
$$\bullet \quad \bullet \quad \bullet$$
$$\bullet \quad \bullet \quad \bullet$$

Coursework: Squash competition

A Squash Club organizes a competition between its members so that each member plays each of the other members. Figure 1 illustrates the number of games which have to be played if there are 15 members in the club. How would you use this diagram to find the number of games which would have to be played?

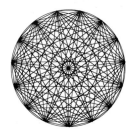

It is not very sensible to count all the lines, so we must devise another method. First we must simplify the problem.

Figure 1

1 If there were three members of the Squash Club, three games would be played:

    A v B, A v C, and B v C

2 If there were four members, A, B, C and D, it would be necessary to play the following games:

    A v B, C v D, D v A, D v B, C v B and A v C

These can be arranged in a logical way like this:

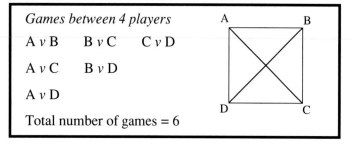

Figure 2

3 **a** Copy Figure 2. Compile a similar diagram showing the games between five players (A, B, C, D, E) and another showing the games between six players (A, B, C, D, E, F).

   b Copy the table below and enter your results from part **a**. Describe the pattern in the sequence. Use the pattern to help complete the table.

No. of members	3	4	5	6	7	8	9	10	11	12	13	14	15
No. of games	3	6											

   c How many straight lines are there in Figure 1?

EXTENSION

4 **a** Work out a rule to give the number of games necessary if there are n members in the competition.

   b How many games would there be if there were 100 members in the competition?

APPENDIX: SETS

Elements of sets

A set is a collection of things, such as a set of golf clubs or a tea set or even a Scottish reel set.

A set is always shown in brackets like these { }. The set of even counting numbers less than 9 is written like this:

$\{2, 4, 6, 8\}$

A member of a set is called an 'element' and is represented by $\in$. In the above set of numbers we can, for example, write:

$2 \in \{2, 4, 6, 8\}$

Sometimes a set does not have any elements in it. It is then called an 'empty set'. This fact can be shown either as $\emptyset$ or { }.

Note that $\{\emptyset\}$ is not an empty set. Can you see why?

Exercise 56

For each question list, in brackets, the elements of the set.

1. $A = \{$Odd numbers less than 12$\}$
2. $B = \{$Prime numbers less than 20$\}$
3. $C = \{$Multiples of 5 up to and including 35$\}$
4. $D = \{$Multiples of 6 up to but not including 36$\}$
5. $E = \{$Triangular numbers less than 20$\}$

6. $F = \{$Factors of 12$\}$
7. $G = \{$First 7 square numbers$\}$
8. $H = \{$Polygons which have fewer than 7 sides$\}$
9. $I = \{$Polygons which have fewer than 3 sides$\}$
10. $J = \{$Triangles with more than one line of symmetry$\}$

11. $K = \{$Numbers on a calculator which look like upside down letters$\}$
12. $L = \{$Football League teams from Manchester$\}$
13. $M = \{$Football League teams from Land's End$\}$
14. $N = \{$Months with 31 days$\}$
15. $O = \{$Days of the week with six-letter names$\}$

___ The n( ) notation

We can show how many elements there are in a set. For example, in the set

$$X = \{1, 3, 5, 8, 9\}$$

there are 5 elements. This is written

$$n(X) = 5$$

___ Exercise 57

Use the $n(\ )$ notation to indicate the number of elements in each of the sets shown in Exercise 56.

___ Describing sets

If the elements of a set are listed they can be described. You must be careful to describe exactly which items are included and which are not. For example, in the set

$$Y = \{\text{Numbers}\}$$

we do not know if the set contains fractions, decimals or negative numbers. But if we write:

$$Y = \{\text{Whole numbers less than 8 but more than 2}\}$$

then the elements in the set are the numbers 3, 4, 5, 6 and 7.

___ Exercise 58

Describe each of the following sets:

1   $A = \{a, e, i, o, u\}$
2   $B = \{v, w, x, y, z\}$
3   $C = \{1, 4, 9, 16, 25\}$
4   $D = \{\text{England, Scotland, Wales, Northern Ireland}\}$
5   $E = \{10, 20, 30, 40, 50, 60\}$

6   $F = \{2, 3, 5, 7, 11, 13\}$
7   $G = \{-1, -2, -3, -4, -5\}$
8   $H = \{\frac{1}{2}, \frac{1}{4}, \frac{1}{8}, \frac{1}{16}, \frac{1}{32}, \frac{1}{64}\}$
9   $I = \{\text{Jack of Hearts, Queen of Hearts, King of Hearts}\}$
10   $J = \{\frac{1}{2}, 2, 4\frac{1}{2}, 8, 12\frac{1}{2}\}$

11   $K = \{4, 6, 10, 14, 22, 26\}$
12   $L = \{1, 2, 5, 10, 20, 50, 100\}$
13   $M = \{1, 2, 3, 4, 6, 8, 12, 24\}$

Venn diagrams

A Venn diagram shows a set, or a number of sets, inside a rectangle. The rectangle is known as the 'Universal set' and is denoted by $\mathscr{E}$. Each set is shown as a circle or other closed figure.

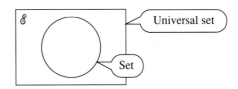

Activity 37

Ann is playing with a 'one-armed bandit'. It costs her 10p a go. With each pull of the handle, any one of the numbers 1 to 14 is equally likely to appear in the window. (For Square numbers, see page 152 Question 6; for Triangular numbers, see page 152 Question 7.)

1 $\mathscr{E}$ = {Counting numbers 1 to 14 inclusive}
T = {Triangular numbers}
S = {Square numbers}

Copy and complete the Venn diagram.
Add the remaining numbers in the correct regions.

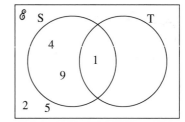

2 **a** If the number to appear is either a Square number or a Triangular number or both, Ann will get her 10p back. The region on the Venn diagram in which these numbers are shown is called the **union** (written $\cup$) of the sets S and T. Copy and complete:

$S \cup T = \{1, 3, \ldots\}$

b If the number to appear is both a Square number and a Triangular number, Ann will win 50p but not get her 10p back. The region on the Venn diagram in which this number appears is called the **intersection** (written $\cap$) of the sets S and T. Copy and complete:

$S \cap T = \{\ \ \}$

c If neither a Square nor a Triangular number appears, Ann will lose her 10p. In 14 goes on the one-armed bandit, how much is Ann likely to lose?

REMEMBER

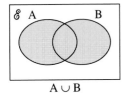

$A \cup B$

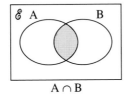

$A \cap B$

NOTE

If the set A **contains** the set B,
then B is a subset (written $\subset$) of A.

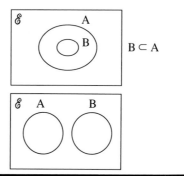

If the sets A and B have no common
elements, the Venn diagram can
be drawn like this.

■ *EXAMPLE 1*

A group of friends go into a chip shop. Alan, Brian, Cathy, David, Erica and Fred all buy chips. Georgina, Erica, Helen, Ian and Jane all buy fish. Kevin is on a diet and so does not buy anything.

Represent this information on a Venn diagram by writing the first letter of each name in the correct place. From your diagram find **a** $C \cap F$ **b** $C \cup F$, where $C = \{$People buying chips$\}$ and $F = \{$People buying fish$\}$.

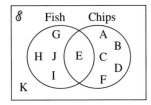

a $C \cap F = \{E\}$
b $C \cup F = \{A, B, C, D, E, F, G, H, I, J\}$

■ *EXAMPLE 2*

$\mathcal{E} = \{1, 2, 3, 4, 5, 6, 7, 8, 9, 10\}$
$P = \{$Prime numbers$\}$
$E = \{$Even numbers$\}$
Draw a Venn diagram and then find **a** $P \cap E$ **b** $P \cup E$

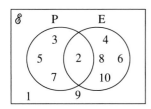

a $P \cap E = \{2\}$
b $P \cup E = \{2, 3, 4, 5, 6, 7, 8, 10\}$

___ Exercise 59

1 $\mathscr{E}$ = {Squash, tennis, badminton, golf, snooker, darts}
R = {Racquet games}
B = {Ball games}
a List the elements in each of sets R and B.
b Draw a Venn diagram to illustrate these sets.
c Use your diagram to find:
(i) $R \cap B$ (ii) $R \cup B$ (iii) $n(R \cap B)$ (iv) $n(R \cup B)$
(v) What does your diagram tell you about darts?

2 $\mathscr{E}$ = {The suit of spades in a normal pack of 52 playing cards}
A = {Picture cards}
B = {Cards with numbers less than 7}
C = {Prime number cards}
D = {Cards with numbers that are factors of 12}
E = {Square number cards}
F = {Triangular number cards}
G = {Red cards}
a List the elements in each of the above sets. (Take an Ace to represent number 1.)
b Draw a separate Venn diagram to illustrate each of the following:
(i) $C \cap D$ (ii) $E \cup F$
(iii) $A \cap G$ (iv) $A \cap E$
(v) $C \cup D$ (vi) $B \cap E$
(vii) $D \cup E$ (viii) $A \cap B$
c Use the notation $n(\ )$ to show how many elements there are in each of the above sets.

3 $\mathscr{E}$ = {Whole numbers from 1 to 10 inclusive}
Z = {ZOG numbers}
Y = {YOG numbers}
This diagram shows sets Z and Y.

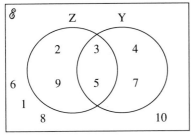

a What type of number is 2?
b What type of number is 4?
c What can you say about the elements in $Z \cap Y$?
d What can you say about the elements in $Z \cup Y$?
e What can you say about 1, 6, 8 and 10?

4 Four squares are fitted together to make the following shapes:

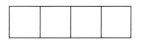 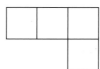 

$\mathcal{E}$ = {Shapes which can be made by fitting four squares together}
T = {Shapes with three squares in a row}
S = {Shapes with one or more lines of symmetry}

Draw a large Venn diagram to illustrate these sets and on it draw each of the four shapes. In words, describe the shape, or shapes, which are in each of the regions:
a $T \cap S$ **b** $T \cup S$

MASTERMINDERS

5 $\mathcal{E}$ = {All types of triangle}
I = {Isosceles triangles}
R = {Right-angled triangles}
Draw a Venn diagram to illustrate these sets and describe a member of each of the four regions.

6 In this Venn diagram each * stands for an element. If $\mathcal{E}$ = {Whole numbers from 1 to 10 inclusive} and sets A and B are both sets of multiples, describe each of the sets A and B as fully as possible.

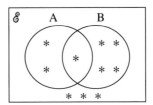

___ n( ) notation and Venn diagrams

Sometimes, instead of writing the individual elements in a Venn diagram, we can put in the numbers of elements. For example, in this Venn diagram,

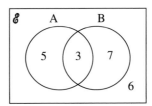

$n(A \cap B) = 3$

$n(A) = 5 + 3 = 8$

$n(B) = 3 + 7 = 10$

> **REMEMBER**
>
> $n(A) = 8$ means that the **number** of elements in A is 8.
> Similarly, $n(A \cap B) = 3$ means that the **number** of elements in the intersection of A and B is 3.

Exercise 60

1 The Venn diagram shows the number of elements in each of the sets. Find:
 a $n(X)$ **b** $n(Y)$
 c $n(X \cap Y)$ **d** $n(X \cup Y)$

For Questions 2 to 9, copy the Venn diagram and replace each ? with the correct number.

2 $n(\mathscr{E}) = 20,\ n(X) = 15,\ n(Y) = 5$

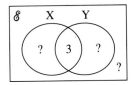

3 $n(\mathscr{E}) = 35,\ n(X) = 15,\ n(X \cup Y) = 26$

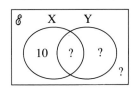

4 $n(\mathscr{E}) = 26,\ n(X) = 19,\ n(Y) = 10$

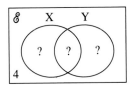

5 $n(\mathscr{E}) = 21,\ n(X) = 9,\ n(Y) = 8,\ n(X \cup Y) = 12$

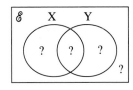

6 $n(\mathscr{E}) = 8,\ n(Y) = 3,\ n(X) = 8$

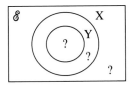

7 $n(\mathscr{E}) = 14,\ n(X \cap Y) = 3,\ n(X) = 10$

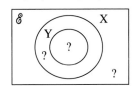

8 $n(\mathscr{E}) = 17,\ n(X) = 5,\ n(Y) = 3$

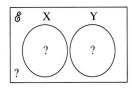

9 $n(\mathscr{E}) = 20,\ n(X \cup Y) = 5,\ n(X) = 3$

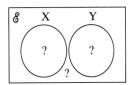

For Questions 10 to 12, draw a suitable Venn diagram to illustrate the given information.

10 In a class of 20 everyone studies at least one language, either French or German. If 12 people study French and 15 study German, how many study both languages?

11 Sheffield Wednesday and Sheffield United played a soccer match. There were 25 000 spectators who supported one or both of the teams. 20 000 supported Sheffield Wednesday. 7000 supported Sheffield United. How many supported both teams?

12 In a class of 20 pupils, 5 play rugby, 10 play soccer and 8 play neither. How many
   a play both games
   b play only soccer
   c play rugby but not soccer?

MASTERMINDER

13 In a class of 28 pupils the number who only play netball is twice the number who only play rounders. The same number play both sports as play neither sport. Find
   a the minimum number who could play netball
   b the maximum number who could play rounders.

___ The complement of a set

The **complement** of a set is everything apart from the set itself. The following diagrams show the region which represents the complement of A (written A').

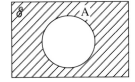 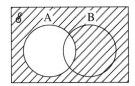

■ EXAMPLE 3
$\mathscr{E} = \{\text{Whole numbers from 1 to 10 inclusive}\}$
$A = \{\text{Even numbers}\}$
List the elements in A'.

This Venn diagram illustrates the information.
$A' = \{1, 3, 5, 7, 9\}$

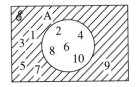

___ Exercise 61

You may not find it necessary to draw a Venn diagram for each question.

1   $\mathcal{E}$ = {Pupils in Westbourne School}
    B = {Boys}
    Describe the elements in B'.

2   $\mathcal{E}$ = {Normal pack of 52 playing cards}
    S = {Cards in the suit of spades}
    Describe the elements in S'.

3   $\mathcal{E}$ = {Capital letters of the alphabet}
    A = {Letters with no axis of symmetry}
    Sketch each member of the set A'.

4   $\mathcal{E}$ = {Whole numbers from 1 to 10 inclusive}
    N = {Numbers less than 4}
    List the members of the set N'.

5   $\mathcal{E}$ = {Whole numbers from 1 to 10 inclusive}
    G = {Numbers greater than or equal to 7}
    List the members of the set G'.

6   $\mathcal{E}$ = {Whole numbers from 10 to 20 inclusive}
    S = {Square numbers}
    List the members of the set S'.

7   $\mathcal{E}$ = {Whole numbers from 1 to 20 inclusive}
    T' = {Numbers bigger than 5 but less than 15}
    List the members of the set T.

8   $\mathcal{E}$ = {Whole numbers from 1 to 20 inclusive}
    S' = {Square numbers}
    List the members of the set S.

9   In a football crowd there are Manchester United, Arsenal and unbiased fans. If $\mathcal{E}$ = {People in the crowd} and M = {Manchester United fans}, describe M'.

10 If $\mathcal{E}$ = {Types of triangles} and S = {Triangles with three lines of symmetry}, list the elements of S'.

MASTERMINDER

11 < means 'is smaller than'. > means 'is bigger than'.
    $\mathcal{E}$ = {Whole numbers from -10 to $+10$ inclusive}
    A = {Numbers < 0}
    B = {Numbers > 0}
    Is it true that $A = B'$ or $A' = B$? Are both statements true, or neither?

175

— Union, intersection and complements

The complement of a set can be used with the union and intersection to define certain parts inside a Universal set.

— *Activity 38*

1 To illustrate $A' \cap B$ on a Venn diagram, we first shade A' and then shade the set B using shading in the opposite direction. The part shaded in both directions is defined by $A' \cap B$.

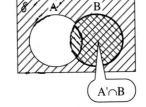

2 Use the same method to illustrate, on separate diagrams, each of the following:
a $A' \cup B$ **b** $A' \cap B'$ **c** $A' \cup B'$

3 Define the shaded area in each of the following:

a 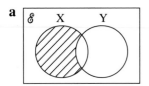   **b**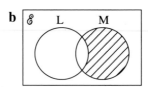

— REMEMBER

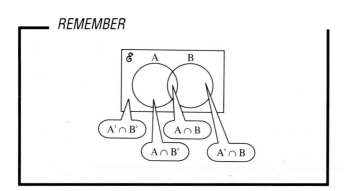

— Exercise 62

1 $\mathscr{E} = \{$Whole numbers from 1 to 6 inclusive$\}$
$S = \{$Factors of 6$\}$
$T = \{$Multiples of 2$\}$
Draw a Venn diagram to illustrate these sets.
Find **a** $S' \cap T$ **b** $S' \cup T'$ **c** $S' \cap T'$ **d** $S \cup T'$

2 $\mathscr{E}$ = {Whole numbers from 1 to 10 inclusive}
X = {Numbers less than 7}
Y = {Numbers bigger than 4 but less than 9}
Draw a Venn diagram for these sets, then find **a** $X' \cap Y$ **b** $X \cup Y'$
c Can you explain what your answers mean?

3 $\mathscr{E}$ = {Eight people who answered a Form 2 survey about musical tastes}
P = {Those who said they preferred pop music}
C = {Those who said they preferred classical music}
The following Venn diagram represents the results of the survey:

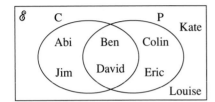

a Find $P' \cap C$ and $P' \cup C$.
b Try to explain what each of these represents.

Brackets in set notation

Brackets ( ) can be used in set notation. Remember that they are always worked out first.

> *NOTE*
>
> In the diagram the shaded region represents $(A \cup B)'$ because it is everything **not** in $A \cup B$.

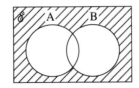

Exercise 63

1 Draw a Venn diagram to illustrate $(A \cap B)'$.

2 $\mathscr{E}$ = {S, Q, U, A, R, E}
A = {A, R, E}
B = {A, S}
Draw a Venn diagram to illustrate this information.
Find **a** $A \cup B$ **b** $(A \cup B)'$ **c** $A \cap B$ **d** $(A \cap B)'$ **e** $A' \cap B'$ **f** $(A' \cup B)'$

3 Draw separate diagrams to illustrate $(A' \cup B)'$ and $A \cap B'$. Comment.

4   $\mathscr{E}$ = {Whole numbers between 1 and 10 inclusive}
    T = {Triangular numbers}
    S = {Square numbers}
    Draw a Venn diagram to illustrate this information.
    Find **a** $(T' \cup S)'$ **b** $(T' \cap S')'$

Problems with three sets

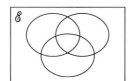

■*EXAMPLE 4*
This Venn diagram shows which of three sports,
hockey (H), rounders (R) and cycling (C), are
enjoyed by 12 children.
a   How many enjoy rounders?
b   Who enjoys rounders and hockey?
c   Who enjoys rounders and hockey but not cycling?
d   Who enjoys all three sports?

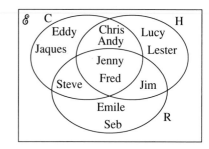

a   The number who enjoy rounders = 6
b   Those who enjoy rounders and hockey = {Fred, Jenny, Jim}
c   One person enjoys rounders and hockey but nor cycling: {Jim}
d   Those who enjoy all three sports = {Fred, Jenny}

Exercise 64

1   In class 3A each pupil was asked if he or she
    liked each of the subjects Mathematics (M),
    Physics (P) and French (F). The results are
    shown on this Venn diagram.
    a Who liked all three subjects?
    b Who liked Maths and Physics but not
      French?
    c Who only liked French?
    d Who didn't like any of the three subjects?

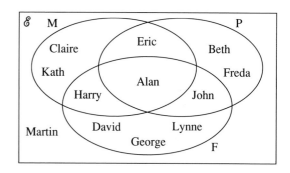

2 $\mathscr{E} = \{P, L, S, M, O, E, T, I, H, G, R, A\}$
$A = \{M, A, R, P, L, E, S\}$
$B = \{H, O, L, M, E, S\}$
$C = \{M, A, I, G, R, E, T\}$
Draw a Venn diagram to show the letters of the names of these great detectives.
Why am I a great detective?

3 Three DIY stores sell various items of DIY equipment.
Grand Mills DIY sells paint, brushes, nails, weed-killer, wallpaper, and wood.
Q and B sells nails, paint, brushes, wallpaper, hammers and screws.
Kansas DIY sells paint, brushes, wallpaper, screws and fencing.
a Illustrate this information on a suitable Venn diagram.
b What items do three stores sell?
c What items do Grand Mills and Q and B but not Kansas sell?
d What items do Q and B and Kansas but not Grand Mills sell?
e What items do Grand Mills and Kansas but not Q and B sell?

4 $\mathscr{E} = \{\text{Whole numbers from 1 to 10 inclusive}\}$
$P = \{\text{Prime numbers}\}$
$S = \{\text{Square numbers}\}$
$T = \{\text{Multiples of 2}\}$
a List the elements of each set.
b Draw a Venn diagram for these sets.
c There are three empty sections on the diagram. What do they represent?

∎ EXAMPLE 5

40 people were asked which topping they liked on their pizzas.
$C = \{\text{People who liked cheese}\}$
$P = \{\text{People who liked pepperoni}\}$
$L = \{\text{People who liked olives}\}$
This Venn diagram represents their replies.

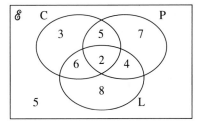

a How many people **only** liked cheese?
b How many people liked cheese?
c How many people liked pepperoni?
d How many people liked all three toppings?
e How many people didn't like any of the toppings?

a The number that liked only cheese = 3.
b The number that liked cheese = 3 + 5 + 2 + 6 = 16.
c The number that liked pepperoni = 7 + 5 + 2 + 4 = 18.
d The number that liked all three toppings = 2.
e The number that didn't like any of the toppings = 5.

___ Exercise 65

1 Thirty children in a junior school were given a test in Arithmetic, English and General Knowledge. Their results are illustrated on the Venn diagram, where:

A = {Those who passed in Arithmetic}
E = {Those who passed in English}
G = {Those who passed in General Knowledge}

a How many passed in each of the three subjects?
b How many passed in one subject only?
c How many passed in only two subjects?
d How many passed in all three subjects?
e How many failed in all three subjects?

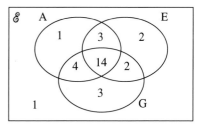

2 The Venn diagram gives the following details about children in a school:

$\mathscr{E}$ = {Children in a mixed school}
B = {Boys in the school}
S = {Children who like sport}
R = {Children who are right-handed}

a How many left-handed children are there?
b How many right-handed girls are there who like sport?
c How many left-handed boys are there who like sport?
d How many children are there in the school?
e How many left-handed girls do not like sport?

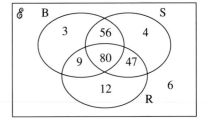

3 A long-distance train carried 250 passengers. Some of the details of the passengers are shown on the Venn diagram.

A = {Passengers who had lunch}
B = {Passengers who had tea}
C = {Passengers who had dinner}

Given $n(A)$ = 110, $n(B)$ = 115 and $n(C)$ = 110, copy and complete the diagram.

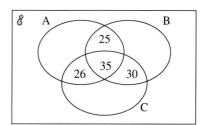

4 40 000 people were asked which television channel, or channels, they watched on a particular day. The results are shown on the table.

Draw a Venn diagram to represent these figures. How many people did not watch any television on the day of the survey?

Viewed	Number (1000's)
BBC only	10
ITV only	15
SKY only	3
BBC and ITV	4
BBC and SKY	3
ITV and SKY	3
BBC, ITV and SKY	1

5 In a small town, 950 houses have a video. 50 houses have a freezer but no garage or video. 30 houses have a garage but no video or freezer. 40 houses have both a freezer and a garage but no video. 10 houses have no garage, no video and no freezer.

$\mathcal{E}$ = {Houses in a small town}
G = {Houses with a garage}
V = {Houses with a video}
F = {Houses with a freezer}

Draw a suitable Venn diagram to represent this information.
How many houses are there in the town?

6 When asked which cartoons they liked, 50 toddlers gave these answers:
10 said they did not like cartoons.
15 said they only liked Mickey Mouse.
3 said they liked Tom and Jerry and Mickey Mouse but not Popeye.
5 said they only liked Tom and Jerry.
Nobody said they liked Tom and Jerry and Popeye but not Mickey Mouse.
Altogether 10 toddlers liked Tom and Jerry and 21 liked Mickey Mouse.
How many only liked Popeye?

7 Given that $n(\mathcal{E}) = 100$, find the value of x.

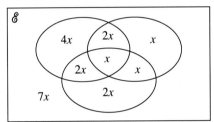

MASTERMINDERS

8 Draw separate Venn diagrams to illustrate each of the following:
   a $(A \cap B) \cup C$ **b** $A \cap (B \cup C)$ **c** $(A \cap B) \cap C$
   d $A \cap (B \cap C)$ **e** $A' \cap B' \cap C'$ **f** $A' \cup B' \cup C'$
   g $(A \cup B)' \cap C$ **h** $(A \cap B)' \cup C$ **i** $A \cup (B \cap C)'$
   j $(A' \cap B') \cup C'$

9 Use set notation to define the shaded regions in each of the following:

a 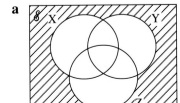 **b** 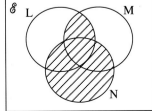 **c**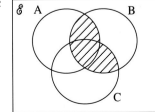

Multiple Choice Test 1

1 Which of the following is smallest?

   a 0.098   **b** 0.1204   **c** 0.12   **d** 0.109 98   **e** 0.123

2 Which of the following is largest?

   a $\frac{1}{8}$ **b** 0.1   **c** $\frac{1}{9}$ **d** $\frac{1}{7}$ **e** $\frac{1}{6}$

3 The approximate answer to 0.355×0.09 is:

   a 3   **b** 0.3   **c** 0.03   **d** 30   **e** 0.003

4 The approximate answer to $51.3 \div 0.45$ is:

   a 100   **b** 10   **c** 0.1   **d** 1   **e** 0.001

5 Work out exactly $9360 \div 90$.

   a 10.4   **b** 1.04   **c** 14   **d** 140   **e** 104

6 The missing number in $6.8 \div \square = 68$ is:

   a 100   **b** 10   **c** 1   **d** 0.1   **e** 0.01

7 How many three-quarter-pint mugs can be filled from a twelve-pint jug?

   a 6   **b** 4   **c** 12   **d** 9   **e** 16

8 Given that $36 \times 72 = 2592$, how many times does 7.2 divide into 259.2?

   a 3.6   **b** 25.92   **c** 36   **d** 360   **e** 72

9 Three eighths of 10.4 m is:

   a 3.9 cm   **b** 39 m   **c** 39 cm   **d** 390 m   **e** 3.9 m

10 Five sixths of a day, measured in hours, is:

   a 4   **b** 10   **c** 15   **d** 20   **e** None of these

11 Find the height of a pile of books if there are 49 books which are each 1.8 cm thick and 11 books which are each 2 cm thick.

   a 110.2 m   **b** 1.102 m   **c** 24.7 m   **d** 0.58 m   **e** 11.02 m

12 The missing number in $68 \times \square = 0.68$ is:

   a 100   **b** 10   **c** 0.1   **d** 0.01   **e** 0.001

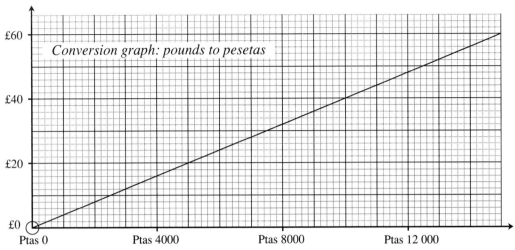

Conversion graph: pounds to pesetas

Questions 13 to 17 refer to this graph.

13 The distance between two adjacent vertical lines represents:

    a Ptas 20   **b** Ptas 200   **c** Ptas 40   **d** Ptas 2000   **e** Ptas 400

14 How many pounds would you expect to change for Ptas 8000?

    a 35   **b** 30   **c** 32   **d** 31   **e** 33

15 How many pesetas would you expect to change for £50?

    a 12 500   **b** 12 000   **c** 13 000   **d** 12 050   **e** 13 000

EXTENSION

16 The exchange rate is £1 to:

    a Ptas 150   **b** Ptas 200   **c** Ptas 220   **d** Ptas 275   **e** Ptas 250

17 How many pounds would you expect to change for 6 million pesetas?

    a 22 000   **b** 220 000   **c** 2400   **d** 24 000   **e** 240 000

18 A tin of beans costs 48p. A packet of biscuits costs 39p. A bottle of lemonade costs 54p. Mrs Ateit bought 3 tins of beans, 7 packets of biscuits and 4 bottles of lemonade. What change did she receive from £10?

    a £6.33   **b** £5.33   **c** £3.67   **d** £4.67   **e** £2.67

19 Work out exactly $\frac{28 \times 39}{52}$.

    a 210   **b** 36   **c** 21   **d** 2.1   **e** None of these

20 A shopper spent one fifth of her money at the butcher's and one third of her money at the supermarket. She had £5.60 left. How much did she start with?

    a £12.30   **b** £11.60   **c** £12   **d** £10.50   **e** £13.20

Multiple Choice Test 2

NOTE

For Chapters 3, 4 and 5. (Ask your teacher if you should do the Extension.)

Calculators are **not** allowed. Do **not** write on this book. Show your working clearly.

Write down the **letter** which you think corresponds to the correct answer.

1 6840 cm equals:

   a 684 m   **b** 684 000 mm   **c** 6.84 km   **d** 68.4 m   **e** 0.684 km

2 To change square centimetres to square metres you:

   a ÷100   **b** ×100   **c** ÷10 000   **d** ÷1000   **e** ×10 000

3 An army tank goes 273 miles using 35 gallons of fuel. The distance it will go on 5 gallons is:

   a 546 miles   **b** 39 miles   **c** 7.8 miles   **d** 191.1 miles   **e** None of these

4 35 per cent of 240 kg is:

   a 84 kg   **b** 840 kg   **c** 8.4 tonnes   **d** 0.84 tonnes   **e** 8.4 kg

5 The ratio of coaches to motorcycles to cars in a car park is 14 : 24 : 210. This ratio simplifies to:

   a 7 : 21 : 210   **b** 14 : 21 : 105   **c** 1 : 3 : 15   **d** 15 : 3 : 1   **e** None of these

6 Ahmed scores 12 out of 40 in a Maths test. This is the equivalent of:

   a 30%   **b** 25/80   **c** 20%   **d** 40%   **e** 25%

7 Six metres of cloth cost £45. How much do five metres cost?

   a £51   **b** £35   **c** £37.50   **d** £54   **e** £54.50

8 A model of a house is 15 cm long. If the house's actual length is 12 m, the model's scale is:

   a 1 : 20   **b** 1 : 40   **c** 1 : 50   **d** 1 : 80   **e** 1 : 125

The diagram represents a rectangular garden with the unshaded area as lawn. All dimensions are shown in metres. Questions 9 and 10 refer to this diagram.

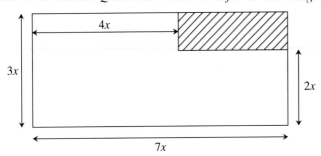

9 The perimeter (distance around the lawn) is:

   a $18x$ metres   **b** $16x$ metres   **c** $19x$ metres   **d** $17x$ metres   **e** $20x$ metres

10 If $x = 3$, the perimeter of the lawn in metres is:

   a 21   **b** 42   **c** 30   **d** 60   **e** 64

11 $15x - 10y + 4x + 13y$ equals:

    a $5x + 17y$ **b** $19x + 17y$ **c** $19x + 3y$ **d** $19x + 23y$ **e** $11x + 3y$

12 When $x = 9$, $y = 12$ and $z = 3$, $xy + xz + yz$ equals:

    a 163   **b** 183   **c** 171   **d** 161   **e** None of these

13 The missing number and/or letter in $\dfrac{9}{y} \times \square = 9$ is:

    a 9   **b** y **c** $9y$ **d** 1   **e** 0

14 In which equation is x equal to 15?

    a $3x = 5$ **b** $\frac{x}{3} = 45$ **c** $15 + x = 30$ **d** $x - 5 = 20$ **e** $\frac{3}{x} = 45$

15 In which equation is x **not** equal to 12?

    a $4x = 48$ **b** $\frac{3}{x} = 36$ **c** $x - 8 = 4$ **d** $24 - x = 12$ **e** $\frac{x}{2} = 6$

EXTENSION

16 Susan, Simon and Sarah share £81 in the ratio $2 : 3 : 4$. Sarah's share is:

    a £18   **b** £27   **c** £9   **d** £36   **e** None of these

17 The plans of a house are drawn to a scale of $1 : 50$. How long should a room be shown if its actual length is 5.5 metres?

    a 11 mm   **b** 10 cm   **c** 110 mm   **d** 100 mm   **e** 110 cm

18 Dave makes an apple pie for ten people and uses $2\frac{1}{2}$ pounds of apples. How many pounds of apples should he use for four people?

    a 2   **b** $1\frac{1}{2}$ **c** 1   **d** $2\frac{1}{2}$ **e** $1\frac{1}{4}$

19 The main span of the Humber Bridge is drawn to scale below. (It is the longest single span in the world.)

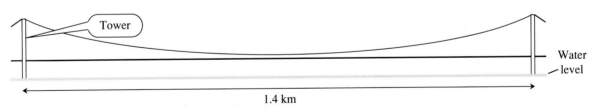

The distance between the towers is 1.4 km. The height of each tower above the water level is approximately:

    a 320 m   **b** 160 m   **c** 16 m   **d** 80 m   **e** 32 m

20 Four fifths of all the trains arriving at Waterloo arrive on time, one tenth arrive early. The percentage which arrive late is:

    a 20%   **b** 10%   **c** 15%   **d** $12\frac{1}{2}\%$ **e** None of these

Multiple Choice Test 3

1 Which has no axis or axes of symmetry?

a b c d e

A special die has faces marked A, B, C, C, D, D. Questions 2 to 4 refer to throwing this die.

2 The probability of throwing an A is:
   a $\frac{1}{6}$ **b** $\frac{2}{6}$ **c** $\frac{1}{3}$ **d** $\frac{1}{2}$ **e** 1

3 The probability of throwing a C is:
   a $\frac{1}{6}$ **b** $\frac{1}{2}$ **c** $\frac{1}{3}$ **d** $\frac{4}{6}$ **e** 0

4 The probability of throwing either a C or a D is:
   a $\frac{1}{2}$ **b** $\frac{2}{3}$ **c** $\frac{5}{6}$ **d** $\frac{1}{3}$ **e** $\frac{2}{6}$

5 A roulette wheel has the numbers 0 to 36 on it. What is the probability of obtaining a number which is not odd?
   a $\frac{19}{36}$ **b** $\frac{18}{37}$ **c** $\frac{1}{2}$ **d** $\frac{19}{36}$ **e** $\frac{19}{37}$

Questions 6 to 10 refer to Figure 1. It is not drawn accurately.

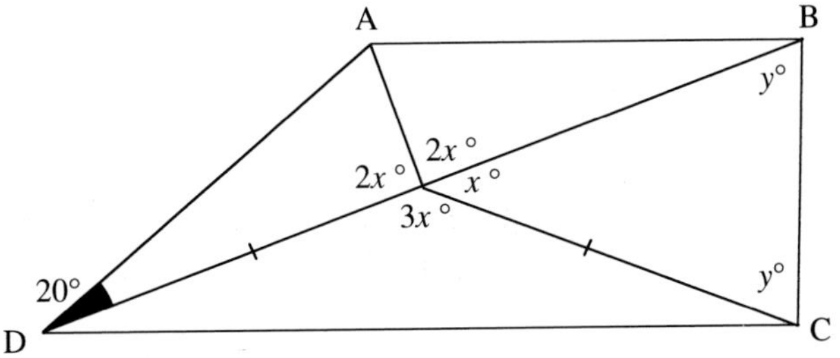

Figure 1

6 The value of x is:
   a 25   **b** 30   **c** 35   **d** 40   **e** 45

7 The value of y is:
   a 77.5   **b** 75   **c** 72.5   **d** 70   **e** 67.5

8 Angle ADC equals:
   a 22.5°   **b** 37.5°   **c** 40°   **d** 42.5°   **e** 45°

9 O is the point in the middle of the figure. DOBC is:
   a A four-sided figure   **b** A scalene triangle   **c** An isosceles triangle   **d** A right-angled triangle   **e** An obtuse-angled triangle

10 Reflex angle ABC is:
   a 272.5°   **b** 275°   **c** 277.5°   **d** 270°   **e** 267.5°

In class 3A there are 20 pupils, five 12-year-olds and fifteen 10-year-olds. Use these facts to answer Questions 11 and 12.

11 The total number of 10- and 12-year-olds in class 3A is:

    a 22   **b** 25   **c** 20   **d** 17   **e** 15

12 The most accurate estimate of the mean age in class 3A is:

    a 11 years   **b** $11\frac{1}{2}$ years   **c** $10\frac{1}{2}$ years   **d** 10 years   **e** $10\frac{1}{4}$ years

13 The angle at the centre of a regular 10-sided figure is:

    a 72°   **b** 45°   **c** 90°   **d** 60°   **e** 36°

14 The mean weight of four girls is 61 kg and the mean weight of five boys is 70 kg. The mean weight of the nine children is:

    a 67.0 kg   **b** 65.5 kg   **c** 65.0 kg   **d** 66.0 kg   **e** 66.5 kg

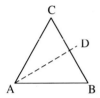

Figure 2

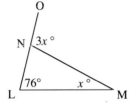

Figure 3

Figure 4

15 In Figure 2, AD is the only axis of symmetry. Which of the following is **not** true?

    a AC = AB   **b** AĈD = AB̂D   **c** AD̂B = 90°   **d** AC = CB   **e** CÂD = BÂD

EXTENSION

16 In Figure 3, the size of the angle MNO is:

    a 38°   **b** 120°   **c** 115°   **d** 108°   **e** 114°

17 Figure 4 shows the face of a clock showing the time at 09:15. The angle between the hands is:

    a 170°   **b** 175°   **c** 172.5°   **d** 177.5°   **e** None of these

18 Nigel has an average of 18 marks from ten tests. To raise his average to 20, the number of marks he must gain in his next test is:

    a 20   **b** 25   **c** 30   **d** 35   **e** 40

19 The ages of six pupils are: 13 yr 6 mth, 12 yr 4 mth, 12 yr 3 mth, 13 yr 6 mth, 13 yr 9 mth, 12 yr 8 mth. Their average age is:

    a 13 yr 0 mth   **b** 12 yr 9 mth   **c** 13 yr 1 mth   **d** 13 yr 2 mth   **e** 13 yr 3 mth

20 On their twelfth birthdays, Jane was 152 cm tall, Jean was 148 cm tall and Anna was 139 cm tall. On their fourteenth birthdays, Jane was 157 cm tall, Jean was 152 cm tall and Anna was 145 cm tall. Their mean increase in height per year was:

    a $2\frac{1}{2}$ cm   **b** 3 cm   **c** $3\frac{1}{2}$ cm   **d** 5 cm   **e** $7\frac{1}{2}$ cm

Multiple Choice Test 4

NOTE

For Chapters 8, 9 and 10. (Ask your teacher if you should do the Extension.)
Calculators are **not** allowed. Do **not** write on this book. Show your working clearly.
Write down the **letter** which you think corresponds to the correct answer.

1 In which equation is x **not** equal to 12?
   a $x - 2 = 10$ **b** $x + 2 = 14$ **c** $3x = 36$ **d** $\frac{x}{4} = 3$ **e** $\frac{4}{x} = 3$

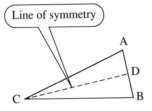

Figure 1

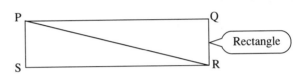

Figure 2

2 See Figure 1. If AB = 7 cm and CD = 13 cm, what is the area of triangle ABC?
   a $91\,cm^2$ **b** $182\,cm^2$ **c** $45.5\,cm^2$ **d** $42\,cm^2$ **e** $45\,cm^2$

3 See Figure 2. If PQ = 4 cm and PS = 9 mm, what is the area of triangle PQR?
   a $36\,cm^2$ **b** $3.6\,cm^2$ **c** $18\,cm^2$ **d** $1.8\,cm^2$ **e** $360\,cm^2$

4 See Figure 1. If CD = 13 mm and area of triangle ABC = $78\,mm^2$, what is the length of AB?
   a 6 mm   **b** 12 mm   **c** 3 mm   **d** 1014 mm   **e** 9 mm

5 See Figure 2. If the area of PQR = $88\,cm^2$ and SR = 11 cm, what is the area of PSR?
   a $8\,cm^2$ **b** $22\,cm^2$ **c** $44\,cm^2$ **d** $11\,cm^2$ **e** $88\,cm^2$

6 The number 11 is a prime factor of:
   a 251   **b** 252   **c** 253   **d** 254   **e** 255

7 The number 7 is a factor of both:
   a 21 and 27   **b** 77 and 84   **c** 37 and 47   **d** 72 and 75   **e** 1 and 7

8 Which of the following numbers is the cube root of 64?
   a 2   **b** 4   **c** 8   **d** 16   **e** 32

9 The lowest number into which both 12 and 18 can be divided is:
   a 24   **b** 72   **c** 48   **d** 60   **e** 36

10 Sound travels at 300 m/s. The sound of an explosion is heard 9 seconds after it occurred. How far away was the explosion?
   a 270 m   **b** 2.7 km   **c** 27 km   **d** 270 000 m   **e** None of these

11 A number written as 2^6 equals:

  a 26   **b** 36   **c** 64   **d** 32   **e** 128

12 The next term in the sequence 9, 12, 16, 21, ... is:

  a 24   **b** 25   **c** 26   **d** 27   **e** 28

13 The nth term in the sequence 7, 8, 9, 10, ... is:

  a n **b** $n+1$ **c** $n+7$ **d** $n+6$ **e** $7n$

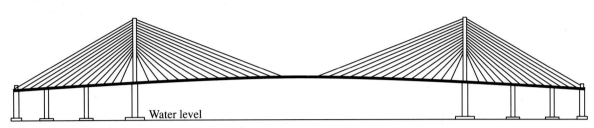

This is a diagram of the bridge across the Thames at Dartford. Questions 14, 15 and 16 refer to this photograph.

14 The distance between the top of each of the towers is 450 m. The scale of the diagram is:

  a 1 : 5   **b** 1 : 50   **c** 1 : 500   **d** 1 : 5000   **e** 1 : 50 000

15 Use your answer to Question 14 to work out the height of each tower above the water level. This is nearest to:

  a 132 m   **b** 137 m   **c** 142 m   **d** 147 m   **e** 152 m

EXTENSION

16 The scale of a diagram of the same bridge is 1 : 200. On this photograph, the highest part of the road above water level is shown as approximately:

  a 3 cm   **b** 10 cm   **c** 20 cm   **d** 30 cm   **e** 40 cm

17 The base area of a rectangular box is 300 cm². If the volume is 1650 cm³, the height is:

  a 4 cm   **b** 4.5 cm   **c** 5 cm   **d** 5.5 cm   **e** 6 cm

18 An InterCity train travels 80 miles in three quarters of an hour. This is approximately:

  a 60 mph   **b** 100 mph   **c** 110 mph   **d** 90 mph   **e** 120 mph

19 A boy walking beside his father takes five steps to his father's three. If they both step off together, they will be in step after:

  a 10 steps   **b** 12 steps   **c** 15 steps   **d** 20 steps   **e** 25 steps

20 Light travels at 300 000 km/s. The Sun is nearly 150 million kilometres from Earth. The time it takes light to reach us from the Sun is approximately:

  a 50 minutes   **b** 5 seconds   **c** 8 hours   **d** 8 minutes   **e** 8 seconds